# HOMEOPATHY & CHAKRAS
## Balancing, Cleansing and Activating Energy Centers with Homeopathy

**Claudia De Rosa**
Classical Homeopath

**B. Jain Publishers (P) Ltd.**
USA — Europe — India

**HOMEOPATHY AND CHAKRA**

First Edition: 2011
1st Impression: 2011

Published by Kuldeep Jain for

**B. JAIN PUBLISHERS (P) LTD.**
1921/10, Chuna Mandi, Paharganj, New Delhi 110 055 (INDIA)
*Tel.:* +91-11-4567 1000 • *Fax:* +91-11-4567 1010
*Email:* info@bjain.com • *Website:* **www.bjain.com**

*Printed in India by*
J.J. Offset Printers

ISBN: 978-81-319-1829-6

## Dedication

To my two wonderful children, Julia and Joshua,
who make my life so fulfilling and special each
and every day in a very special way.

# Preface

> *First there was one, the Source of All,*
> *The Creator Seed.*
> *In stillness it rested.*
> *Then there was two. From the two the many formed.*
>
> *(The Holy Bible)*

The book will not be a summary of the voluminous extant literature available about chakras and energy healing, nor will it be a parroting of such.

I believe that true understanding of the healing process in continuity, with integrity, defeats the disease of *ego* and *arrogance*. Without this direct experience we are stabbing in the dark. Hence ancient healing sciences were holistic, they took into consideration the origin of life and creation in order to understand self, the life energy, the nature of existence and in order to heal disease.

Physics tells us that nothing can move without voltage, a vector or energetic force and direction (intelligence). This polar energy is often 'represented', symbolized, or characterized by *yin and yang, shakti and shiva, ida and pingala, left and right, earth and sky, front and back, nature and spirit, being and consciousness,* right brain/left brain, subjectivity/objectivity, respectively.

This "relationship" and its myriad energetic circuits upholds life and potentiates creativity when it is in harmony and synchrony, but when it is corrupted, fragmented, blocked, obfuscated, and distorted disease patterns arise and impact negatively upon the energy body organization, mental organization, and the physical organism as well.

This study of the movement of the energy and how the energy vibrates in gross and subtle forms, how it flows, pulsates, and resonates in the human body, how it is harmonized and organized intelligently on one hand and on the other how it is corrupted and creates disease, inhibition, fragmentation, and dysfunction is the subject of indigenous wholistic sciences of healing which mostly have become forgotten in the West, but which have survived in the East in forms of yoga, tantra, taoism, chi gong, acupuncture, and so forth.

When this energy direction *(intelligence)* is out of harmony with Source and Manifestation, Spirit and Nature, Head and Root, Crown and Earth, then it is also corruptive to the physical body. Creative energy is inhibited and misdirected into destructive and pathological behaviour while specific tensions, conflicts, and stress (called dis-ease) can be discerned and articulated.

The life supporting intelligent energy is innate in all of creation *(shakti)*. Very importantly that means it is inside of all of us (dormant, suppressed, and dissociated as it may be). So, as we study energy healing if it is to be honest and effective, we must also be willing to take on the authentic spiritual journey to know our 'self' and look inside. *In other words, if one is not ready to look inside, then no true knowledge or functionality in this realm can be achieved.*

Thus, the direction of healing for most of us is to invite this innate intelligent energy to take its rightful place in our life, but in order for this self healing to occur usually the conditioned "mind" or left brain reinforced belief system has to move out of the way to allow for this. Thus, the direction of healing (in time and space) is for most of us an indigenous movement from the inside out and earth chakra upward versus one imposed by logic (top down) or from outside authorities (outside to inside). The basic impediment that must be over come is our incessant imposition of the veil of ignorance upon the profound and sacred organic interaction of creator/creation. This veil of sorrow is reinforced by core beliefs, habits, past imprints, past trauma, negative conditioning, false assumptions, bias, prejudice, fear, and all the rest of what are called in classic yogic terminology: *kleshas, samskara, vasana, vrtti, or avidya.* Regardless of the language or terminology in which to peer into the nature of disease, we will see the same underlying common currents.

I believe that *healing is a process* (not a singular event), a journey, an opportunity and disease is the cure in progress. It is the mechanism by which the whole body (the physical and the spiritual body) asserts itself and communicates its needs. It is a dynamic process and so it's life.. and so it's our Spirit and our Soul.

The beginner can be easily seduced by the plethora of various terminology, charts, external authoritative systems, and techniques that deal with the subject, and they often make the mistake to attempt to memorize, conform to, and parrot them. But my warning is that healing lies in the opposite direction, connecting up with one's own intelligent energy body. I hope the following will give some encouragement to this 'exploration'.

**Claudia De Rosa**

# Publisher's Note

Homeopathy is a healing form of treatment which is increasing its spread, far and wide. It is also being connected to many other healing sciences. The study of—Chakras—is another spiritual science which is being used in many parts of the world as one of the modes of healing the human body.

Claudia De Rosa is a homeopathic practitioner who has used the spiritual aspect of the study of chakras. She links the diseases to the imbalance and disharmony in life and explains how the healing process is about bringing a continuity and integrity which thus, removes diseases.

This is a first attempt to publish the linkage of—Homeopathy and the study of chakras—together. The book covers the various aspects of—chakras, colours, homeopathy and—how the author has used all these sciences for treating various ailments. We hope that in this time of integrative medicine—this book brings a new aspect to health and healing.

**Kuldeep Jain**
C.E.O., B Jain Publishers (P) Ltd.

# About the Author

Claudia De Rosa is a Classical Homeopath, School Director of the British Institute of Homeopathy for the Republic of Ireland and Founder of Vis Vitalis Education, Italian provider of homeopathic training.

"Thanks to constant travelling due to my family's job, I consider myself lucky to have had the opportunity to have studied homeopathy in three different Colleges: Ireland, UK and Italy. I have experience in the treatment of learning and behavioral disorders, autistic spectrum disorder, allergies and food intolerances, panic attacks, teenager's age, childhood, menopause, pregnancy.

Nutritionist and Iridologist with pharmaceutical background, I turned to Homeopathy and to teaching because I passionately believe in the homeopathic way of promoting health and curing sickness. I was using and practicing homeopathy long before I was officially qualified. I was teaching it before I graduated. It seemed everything I had ever done led to this astonishing encounter. It involved science as well as spirit. It involved soul as well as body. It brought me the link I had been unknowingly seeking all of my life. I had found my passion. I had come home. I lived in Cork for over 10 years and I still make frequent fly-backs to run BIH Ireland and so that my two wonderful children, Julia and Joshua, can visit home.."

For more info please visit *www.claudiaderosa.com*

# Contents

# Reference Pictures

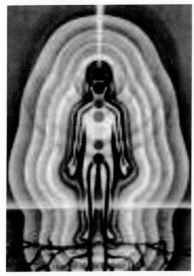

Fig. 1.1: Primary bodies or auric layers and the 7 main chakras

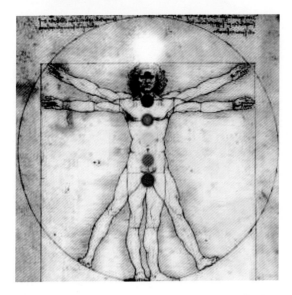

Fig. 1.2: Leonardo da Vinci's Vitruvian Man and 7 Chakras

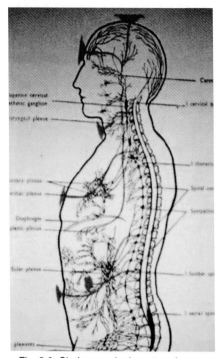

Fig. 2.6: Chakras and relevant sushumna

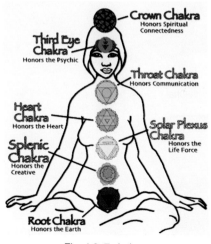

Fig. 4.3: 7 chakras

Fig. 4.8: Colour spectrum

Fig. 5.9: First Chakra

Fig. 5.10: Second Chakra

Fig. 5.11: Third Chakra

Fig. 5.12: Fourth Chakra

Fig. 5.13: Fifth Chakra

Fig. 5.14: Sixth Chakra

Fig. 5.15: Seventh Chakra

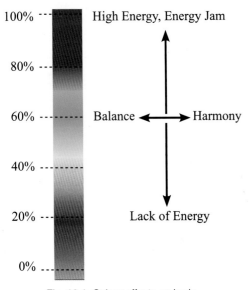

Fig. 10.1: Colour effects on body

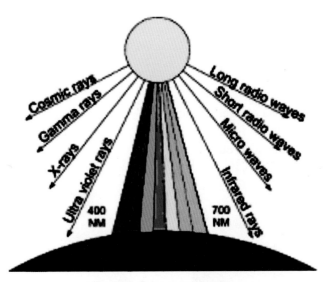

Fig. 10.2: Colours wavelenghts

# Chapter 1

# Introduction

Humans are children of the cosmos. All our organs correspond to energies fluctuating in the cosmos. According ancient teachings subtle worlds of the cosmos create our individual bodies. Like the Universe, our energetic system consists of *seven worlds*, and has *seven primary bodies (or auric layers)* that interact with each other. These bodies consist of the energy of the corresponding universal worlds accordingly, deal with them, and receive the energetic information from them.

Besides the physical bodies, our individual energy system consist of *ether, astral, mental, karmic, intuitive, nirvana, and absolute* subtle energetic bodies, which form our aura - human energy field or bio-energy system. We call energetic bodies subtle because it is difficult to perceive them with our senses. Nevertheless, we can perceive them when specially trained and used bio-energy methods and techniques.

All subtle bodies in a human energy system communicate

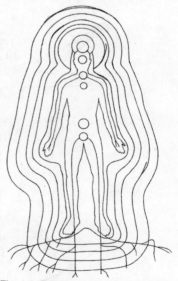

Fig. 1.1: Primary bodies or auric layers and the 7 main chakras
(Refer plate I for Colour picture)

with each other, and with the physical body, through the energetic 'transformers'- chakras.

Chakras transform cosmic universal life-support energies into human energy systems. In Sanskrit, the chakra is a wheel of life. Indian tradition considers invisible chakras as centers of consciousness. All humans have chakras whether we aware of them or not. Chakras are, in fact, centers of different levels of consciousness, ranging from almost bodily to highly spiritual.

Healthy chakras spin all the time bringing energy to the physical body and all its energy layers. Chakras play a very important role in well-being and health. Chakras are an important part of bio-energy systems. The locations and functions of the major chakras are closely related to the endocrine system and autonomic nervous system. The chakras are located on the spinal column, the head, and one chakra is located in the heart plexus.

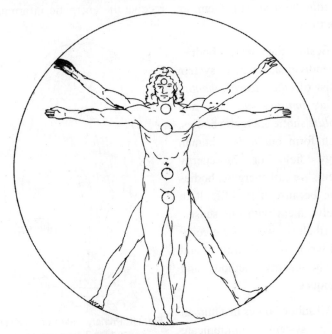

Fig. 1.2: Leonardo da Vinci's Vitruvian Man and 7 Chakras
(Refer plate I for Colour picture)

To heal, is to bring the chakras into alignment and balance, then understand the nature of creation and your purpose in it.

Ever since I was young I have been fascinated by the idea of subtle energy. I can remember as a child discovering a book on yoga, and being fascinated by the descriptions of the chakras, and exotic and mysterious sounding things such as 'prana' and 'kundalini'. In my early twenties this eventually led me to practice yoga, to learn about nutrition, shatsu, massage and colour-therapy, to pharmaceutical studies and aromatherapy and finally to homeopathy.

I had been working with chakras and auras for a while when I came across homeopathy. When I heard about the process of homeopathic dilution it immediately struck me that homeopathy was a system of energy medicine. I thought 'Wow! This makes so sense!'

The only thing that I discovered astonished me was Hahnemann's concept of Vital Force because for a system of medicine that only makes sense if one takes on board the concept of energy, there was remarkably little energy theory. Certainly compared to systems like Ayurvedic medicine or Traditional Chinese Medicine (TCM) which have incredibly detailed and sophisticated energy theory, homeopathy seemed very lacking.

So, if you ask people how they would describe energy the answers people give are usually along the lines of 'energy', 'life force', and 'resonance'. And if you go on to ask homeopaths how exactly they think the vital force operates within the human body, generally people haven't a clue. There is generally little understanding of what exactly the vital force is, or what it does; of exactly what energy is; of what the human energy body is; or of what the relationship is between the energy and physical bodies.

We did once have a detailed understanding of energy in the west.

If one strips away cultural variations, one is left with a core energy model. Or, in fact, two core energy models. One is the Chinese system, practiced in China (obviously!), Vietnam, Cambodia, Laos,

Korea and Taiwan. It is the system that uses the meridians and the five elements of Metal, Wood, Fire, Water and Earth. The other is the Indo-European energy model, so called because it originated somewhere within the Indo-European region. It is based upon the Chakras and the five elements of Ether, Air, Fire, Water and Earth. It is worth noting here that while most people think of the Chakras as Indian, they are also used other cultures as far afield as the Inca Shamans in South America. This model is practiced from Tibet and Mongolia through to the Indian subcontinent the Middle East, Europe, North Africa and the Americas. This is a huge area. An interesting fact for homeopaths here is that, this area coincides with those cultures who used Fly Agaric mushroom, known to us as the homeopathic remedy Agaricus. Some sources believe that the Ayurvedic texts were dictated by the god Soma. Priests used to commune with the god by the ritual use of Agaricus. This area is also the region that Shamanism has been practiced in. Shamans also understand the five elements (sometimes referred to by shamans as the five directions of North, South, East, West and Inner). We know from cave paintings that Shamanism has been practiced for at least 30,000 years and is probably *much* older still. It is our oldest system of knowledge.

The energy model is our birthright. It is what our ancestors would have known and understood for hundreds upon hundreds of generations. It is also what has underpinned formal healing systems including ancient Greek and Egyptian medicine. With the rise of Christianity it became suppressed along with most of our herbal knowledge. Practitioners were persecuted. The knowledge went underground and survived in secret Gnostic sects (gnosis, meaning hidden knowledge). It enjoyed a rebirth in the Middle Ages as humoural medicine, thanks largely to Thomas Aquinus' revival of Greek philosophy3. It faded again during the so-called 'Age of Enlightenment', with the rise of scientific rationality. Most recently it has started to emerge again with the growth of 'New Age' philosophy. However there is nothing New Age about it, and in fact it has never completely gone away. For example our language is full of elemental wisdom. We talk about 'head in the clouds', 'feet of clay', 'stuck in the mud', 'all fired up', 'airy fairy', 'wishy washy' to name but a few of hundreds of examples. Clients and students already know (even if they don't know that they know) what an airy person is like. Or a fiery, watery or earthy person. In doing brainstorms with groups when teaching, people uncover very detailed knowledge about the elemental types, even down to organ weaknesses and disease predispositions.

So what can knowing the model do for homeopathy? As well as explaining how homeopathy works, a conscious knowledge of the model makes remedy selection easier and can even open up whole new avenues of treatment. It can make learning remedies easier as once you understand the energetic essence of a remedy most of its symptoms become predictable and make sense. In fact, the implications for homeopathy are actually vast, too vast to fully explore here. So I am going to concentrate on two areas, one is the five element theory and the other is the relationship between energy and matter. Also by knowing the clear simple truths about how energy works we become less prone to superstition and clutter in homeopathy.

# Chapter 2

# What is Energy?

If you have become interested in this book is because you believe in an Energy System regulating our body or you believe everything has got a form of energy within.

So, what is Energy and how can it heal?

Webster's Dictionary describes Energy as *'a vigorous exertion of power'*.

If we go to Quantum Physics, we find that the concept of Energy gets to be quite complicated. Einstein showed us that E=MC, Energy equals Mass times the speed of Light squared. This tells us that Mass and Energy are interchangeable. And that both space and time are not absolute. The most important consequence of this is that Mass is nothing but a form of Energy. So, everything is a form of Energy, objects at rest have stored Energy. Trees, Rocks, Dogs, Water and People are all made up of Energy, in one form or another.

This means that Energy can exist as either solid matter or as non-solid matter, such as a beam of light. Radio waves, microwaves and X-rays are all forms of pure non-solid Energy.

Energy is all around us, everywhere in all different wavelengths and frequencies. From Energies with very short wavelengths like Cosmic Radiation and X-rays to very long wave lengths such as Radio waves and Infra Red waves.

Everyday our bodies are being hit with these Energies from many different sources. We don't see it but we know it is there.

When we speak, our voice saying words has released sound waves of Energy causing ripples in the air around us. When we think, our brains release wavelengths of Energy.

To the Scientific community, Energy is something measurable with specific instruments to detect for example, heat, light, or cosmic radiation. The Energy used in Healing is equally real, with the measuring device being that exquisitely sensitive one, the human body. Our bodies are receiving stations for Energy and also transmitters of Energy.

We all are made up of a multi-body system, not just the physical body. We have an *Etheric Body, an Emotional Body, a Mental Body and an Astral Body*. Things don't just affect us physically; we are affected on all levels. When we think thoughts, these non-solid forms of Energy go out into our multi system body and greatly affect us.

We all have storage centers in our bodies that store Energy and Energy patterns. They are called Chakras. We can have Energy Patterns stored from events that happened yesterday as well as from many years ago. Some of these patterns will be happy memories and some of them will be unpleasant and painful memories of something that happened to us. Sometimes we stash them away deep into some recess in our Chakras and in our Auras (the Energy field around us), and try to forget about them, but they don't really go away. Dis-ease is a manifestation of unbalanced Energy. Healing, then is a way of balancing Energy.

Throughout our lives we pick up negative forms of Energy, such as Fear, Doubt, Anger, Judgment, Criticism, Blame and others. Any techniques we find that enable us to let go of these patterns will help to move us toward peace and happiness.

The first time I read about the vital force was about the Kirlian method, the technique of using electromagnetic impulse to visualize through photography emotional, mental and physical changes in the person, the *aura* of a person. Hahnemann calls it *Lebenskraft*, Latin called it *Animus or Vigor Vitae,* the Vital Force is what animates our body.

The Chinese call it *Chi,* the Japanese *Hara,* the Indian *Chakras.* It controls all of the body's natural processes and preserves balance. When it becomes inactive, we die.

In homeopathic philosophy, the Vital Force is seen as elemental and indivisible , which means it reacts as a whole to any irritant. If an irritant is strong enough, it can produce a stable derangement of the vital force itself which is the disease.

Because the Vital Force is elemental, it can sustain only one kind of derangement (disease) at a time. Such a derangement may somehow dull the ability of the Vital Force to recognize what is wrong and that, in turn, causes a chronic illness.

Although the Vital Force may have the power to 'throw off' such an illness, it may fail to do so because it lacks perception of the problem. The Vital Force is the essential to our being and makes the symptoms be felt on all levels, physical, mental and emotional.

In aphorism 3 of the *Organon,* Hahnnemann says ays that in order to achieve these goals the physician must know how to apply the forces of nature, to know medicines and their interactions and how to use the ill-disease gently and effectively.

In other words, the physician needs to understand all aspects of human nature, from the gene to the psyche, and must be able to understand the phenomena of disease from beginning to end.

Most importantly the physician must understand the Vital Force, the energy in a person that keeps him alive and passes life to the next generation. It is the force that heals and which maintains the body healthy. Its nature is a mystery.

In aphorism 9 and 11 Hahnemann talks of an energy *(dynamis)* that gives life to the body, that governs all the body's functions without exception and that creates a harmonious whole.

The organism infact is absolutely able to keep itself 'healthy'. It can correct homeostatic balance and repair tissues or direct energy where is required. It is able to heal itself and if not there must be something wrong with the coordinating process ( the Vital Force).

So there is only one possible disease: the disturbance of the Vital Force. It is thrown in disharmony when its curative action is undermined.

Homeopathic remedies directly affect the Vital Force. Because the Vital Force perceives a homeopathic remedy as a disease producing irritant and because the irritant is strong enough, it stirs the Vital Force into action to repeal it. If the disease state produced by the remedy is similar to the disease the Vital Force recognizes the similarity and, in repelling the remedy irritant, it also repels the disease. In effect, the remedy gives the Vital Force a global view of itself in a mirror.

I like the way Dr. Rajan Sankaran explains the concept of the Vital Force. He uses a metaphor of a pole that has several vines growing and wrapping around it. Even though we may not be able to see the pole itself, we know it is because without it the vines would fall to the ground. We can remove one vine, then another, then another, until we think we have removed them all, but they will grow right back and will continue to grow back as long as the pole remains in place to support them.

The pole represents the central disturbance within the Vital Force and the vines represents the disease. By observing the shape of the vines on the pole (the characteristics of the symptoms) we can ascertain the shape of the pole itself (the general characteristics of the inner disturbance). We then can find a remedy that causes the most similar derangement in a healthy person. This remedy is administered in homeopathic form and eventually will stimulate the action of the Vital Force. The Vital Force will remove the disturbance (the pole) and all the individual diseases will get cured.

The main role of the Vital Force then is to maintain the integrity of the whole person, the balance in the individual.

When the integrity of the whole is disturbed, the role of the Vital Force is to correct or recover that integrity.

Four are the principles that determine the degree of ill health:
1. The *vitality* or MOMENTUM.
2. The *exciting cause* or DISTURBANCE.
3. The *predisposition* or SUSCEPTIBILITY.
4. The *inheritance* or MIASM.

In the 'Organon' Hahnemann discusses all different kind of diseases:

* *Real disease* which is an untunement of the Vital Force
* *Apparent disease* is due to some external cause, such as a coffee causing insomnia. When the cause is removed, the disease is caused by drugs or even by remedies (provings, for example). Artificial disease can eliminate natural diseases if their symptoms are similar and stronger ( a stronger dissimilar disease).

Contrary to allopathic method, the homeopath doesn't labels a disease because each Vital Force is unique in the patterns it produces. When we are ill we produce different patterns of illness. If we consider for examples two patients with bronchitis, even if they will show the common symptoms of the disease they will also show individual complaints (symptoms), characteristic of their own constitution. The same if we consider an epidemic disease such a common cold. If we consider a family group, for instance, we will see that in the same group the father will catch a strong cold with chills and sneezing, the three years old son will have runny nose, the sic years old will develop a cold with stuffed nose and the mother will eventually complain about headache due to a nasal congestion. Each one of them will show different symptoms and different intensity of the pain because their individual Vital Force will have a personal and individual manifestation.

That is why it is not possible to measure the untunement of the Vital Force but only to see its manifestations. The untunement can be transferred from one generation to another. Psychological disturbances can dis-regulate the Vital Force.

And so:

➢ The Vital Force is an internal vital energy present in every organism ( humans, animals, plants, etc):

Fig. 2.1

➢ The Vital Force is an external energy present in different intensities, colours and shapes around a body that protects the whole body, in all its parts, from external disturbances.

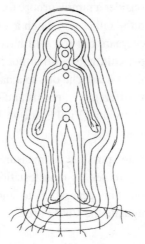

Fig. 2.2: (See Plate...... for colour reference)

➢ The Vital Force is a scale: when the vital force is in balance there is health.

Fig. 2.3: Balace of Life

➢ The Vital Force is like sound waves: it can change intensity \ every time tries to bring the body in its whole back to balance

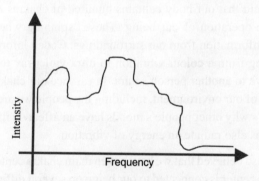

Fig. 2.4: Relation between intensity and Frequency of Vital Force

Therefore there are many ways to balance our Energy:

A. One approach is to become the most complete and loving being you can be. The loving Energy will naturally dissolve the parts of you that are keeping you unbalanced.

B. Another way of balancing your Energy is through:

1. Recognition—recognizing the problem.

2. Surrender and Release—putting trust in the highest power, letting go of trying to control how your life will manifest. It is releasing how we think things should be, and knowing that he Divine Source will take control.

If you combine both paths of A: Love and B: the path of Release, you will have the fastest way possible to a balanced, healed state of being.

Also a person can collect energy from several different levels of vibrations, including colour, that are utilized in various parts of the body. Throughout our body we have main energy centers, which are connected to major organs or glands that govern other body parts. Each of these main energy centers are referred to as chakra–chakra is a Sanskrit word which means wheel. A chakra is a wheel-like spinning vortex that whirls in a circular motion forming a vacuum in the center that draws in anything it encounters on its particular vibratory level.

It is said that our body contains hundred of chakras that are the key to the operation of our being. These "spinning wheels" draw-in coded information from our surroundings. Coded information can be anything from a colour vibration to ultra-violet ray to a radio or micro wave to another person's aura. In essence our chakras receive the health of our environment, including the people we are in contact with (that's why other people's moods have an affect on us!). As well our chakras also radiate an energy of vibration.

It is also believed that we have seven main chakra centers and that each main center is connected to our being on several different levels: physical, emotional, mental and spiritual. On the physical level each chakra governs a main organ or gland, which is then connected to other body parts that resonate the same frequency.

Every organ, gland and body system is connected to a chakra and each chakra is connected to a colour vibrational frequency. For example, the heart chakra governs the thymus gland and it is also in charge of the functioning of the heart organ, lungs, bronchia system, lymph glands, secondary circulatory system, immune system as well as the arm and hands. And the heart chakra resonates to the colour green.

The seven main chakra centers are aligned along the spinal column. If there are disturbances on any level, this shows in the chakra's vitality level. Also each of the seven main chakras is their own intelligence center. This means that each chakra is not only associated with our physical health but also controls aspects connected to our emotional, mental and belief system.

To help balance a chakra–whether on an emotional, intellectual, physical or spiritual level–we need to bring in the chakra (colour) vibration, which resonates at the same frequency. But will see this in detail later on.

In the Chakra System the most important and fundamental forms of energy enter the human system through the Root and Crown chakras. These two chakras are connected by a nadi called, *sushumna*..

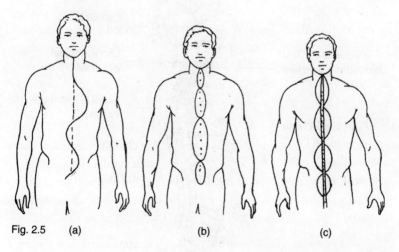

Fig. 2.5      (a)                          (b)                          (c)

The *sushumna* runs up and down the central axis of the body within the spine, between the crown (top of the head) and sacrum. The sushumna is also connected to all seven primary chakras via the 'stems', which provides each chakra with this vital energy.

This primary current runs "between the sun and earth" - "from heaven above and earth below."

As Above, So Below.

This current induces other currents at right angles to itself, which flow between the spine and the outer edges of our etheric body (aura.) Thus we have a vital etheric body consisting of an interweaving mesh of stream of energy with the spinal current as an axis. This axis actually holds the "etheric body" (our aura) together and gives it coherent form. Think of this like a magnet surrounded by lines of force in which the metal fillings are drawn into a pattern and held in place in a magnetic field.

*At the center of each chakra, in its deepest point, there is a stem-like channel that extends to the spine and merges with it. The chakras are connected to the sushumna via these stems, which provides each chakra with "vital energy."*

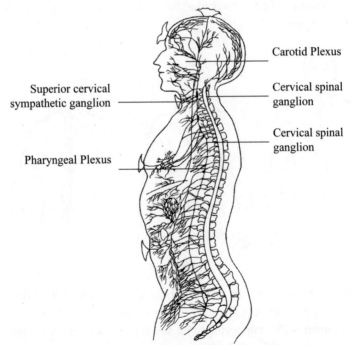

Carotid Plexus

Superior cervical sympathetic ganglion

Cervical spinal ganglion

Cervical spinal ganglion

Pharyngeal Plexus

Fig. 2.6: Chakras and relevant sushumna (Refer Plate II for Colour picture)

Besides the sushumna, there are two additional energy channels that play an important role in our energy system. These channels are known in Sanskrit as: *"ida" and "pingala."*

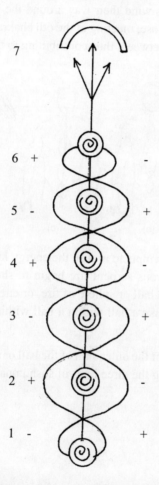

Fig. 2.7: The Ida and Pingala ascend and decend in aspiral pattern, contributing to the chakras' spin. The Sushumna trends up the center

The *pingala channel* is the carrier of solar energy. It is full of heat and drive. It begins on the right hand side of the Root chakra and ends in the upper area of the right nostril.

The *ida channel* is the carrier of the cool and calming lunar energy. It begins on the left hand side of the Root chakra and ends in the left nostril.

These two channels wind their way around the sushumna from the Root chakra to the nose, meeting at the 6th chakra and polarizing each of the chakras in between, thus contributing to their spin.

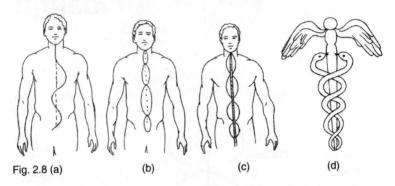

Fig. 2.8 (a)          (b)          (c)          (d)

Only when one attempts to arouse the energy latent in the inner layers does the dangerous serpent fire begin to show itself. Think of this serpent fire as a ball or sphere of fire, or energy, and the ball is made up of layers, like a ball within a ball within a ball within a ball, etc.

The harmless fire of the outer skin of the ball or sphere travels up the spinal column using the three lines of sushumna, ida and pingala simultaneously.

# Chapter 3

# What is Kundalini?

Kundalini is an invisible force, but in the human body it is clothed in a nest of hollow concentric spheres of astral and etheric matter, one within the other.

There are seven concentric spheres resting within the Root Chakra (in an around the last hollow of the spine close to the coccyx.) In the ordinary human, the only force active is the outermost sphere; the other spheres are asleep.

In order to bring your Root Chakra (the 1st) into full activity is to awaken these inner spheres, and it is this force that arouses or awakens (activates) the rest of the chakras.

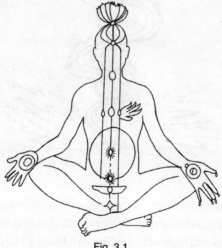

Fig. 3.1

The kundalini power lies at rest at the lower end of the spine like a "coiled snake" and enters the system through the Root Chakra. The kundalini power flows through the sushumna in a mere trickle in most people. But when it is awakened, it rises up the sushumna like a growing stream, activating the chakras, supplying them with vibrations, causing them to expand and increase their vibrational frequency.

Fig. 3.2

As the kundalini rises, its energy is transformed into various vibrations, corresponding to each individual chakra (i.e. it is lowest at the Root Chakra and highest at the Crown Chakra.) The degree of each chakra's performance is determined by the degree of consciousness (awareness) the person has attained in the various areas of his/her life, and whether they are blocked by stress and / or unresolved experiences. The more conscious a person is, the more active and open their chakras will be and the more kundalini that will be able to enter their body and flow like a strong flowing stream.

1. When the serpent-fire is awakened in the person at the "astral" level, it moves on to the Sacral (2nd) chakra, which corresponds to the physical spleen, and through it, vitalizes the whole astral body.

2. Then it moves on to the Solar Plexus (3rd) chakra, vivifying it, awakening in the astral body the power of feeling, a sensitivity to all sorts of influences.

3. Then it moves on to the Heart (4th) chakra, which when awakened endows the person with a power to comprehend and sympathize with the vibrations of other astral entities in a way that they can instinctively understand something of their feelings.

4. Then it moves on to the Throat (5th) chakra, awakening/activating it, giving the person the power of hearing on the astral plane.

5. Then it moves on to the 6th - Third Eye chakra, which when developed and awakened (activated) produces astral sight.

6. Finally, when it awakens or activates the Crown - Third Eye (7th) chakra, which corresponds to the top of the head, it completes the astral life.

Vague, huh?

Let's learn more about Chakras then!

# Chapter 4

# Chakras

There is considerable confusion about "Chakras", not the least of which is the fact that almost no two "systems" you read about seems to be the same. Some have seven chakras, some have more, some call each chakra one thing, some call them another.

Fig. 4.1

Without entering into an exposition of all the systems, which almost inevitably turns into a defense of one or the debunking of another, suffice it to say that there are many different chakra systems, brought about by many cultures and epochs, for different reasons and with different objectives. Here we will limit ourselves to the introduction of only one system, the "classic" Tantric system of "inner" chakras associated with Yoga and Hindu thought. We will call this one the "Primary" chakra system, as it is known.

For the sake of clarity and dispelling some confusion, we will make a simple "comparison" of this system with the one most commonly known in the West, which we can generically describe as the "New Age" chakra system, since there are an infinite number of names and variations of this one as well. We will call this one the "Secondary" chakra system, as this appears to be the accepted term.

We shall very clearly state that we neither endorse nor reject either of them, as we feel that all of these "systems" have their distinct origins, objectives, and reasons for being, and it is up to each individual to decide what is best for yourself or what serves your purposes.

It is said that when you begin to develop your senses, a new and fascinating world opens before you; the hidden world suddenly unveils itself - your perception heightens and your thoughts and feelings are expressed before your very own eyes in colour and form.

There is more to the human body than the physical body. Unfortunately, most people consider the physical body and the material world to be the only reality that exists. They believe this because for them, these are the only things that can be discerned with their own physical senses, and I might add, understood by their rational mind. But there are numerous energy bodies within and around the human body. These energy bodies are:

1. The ethereal body.
2. The emotional (astral) body.
3. The mental body.
4. The spiritual body.

Each energy body possesses its own vibrational frequency, from the lowest (ethereal) to the highest (spiritual).

In addition, there is a complex energy system that is at work, which the body could not exist without. This energy system consists of energy bodies, namely:

1. The chakras (or energy centers).
2. The nadis (also known as energy channels).

Nadi is a Sanskrit word meaning, "pipe" or "vein." Nadis are akin to a network of channels or arteries that transport prana (vital energy) throughout the human being's energy system.

Ancient Indian texts say there are 72,000 nadis in the human body, whereas other archaic texts speak of 350,000 nadis. The most important nadis are called:

1. Sushumna.
2. Ida.
3. Pigala.

The nadis of one energy body are connected to the nadis of the neighbouring energy body via the chakras.

The seven main chakras are described as being aligned in an ascending column from the base of the spine to the top of the head. Each chakra is associated with a certain colour, multiple specific functions, an aspect of consciousness, a classical element, and other distinguishing characteristics.

The chakras are thought to vitalise the physical body and to be associated with interactions of both a physical and mental nature. They are considered loci of life energy, or prana, which is thought to flow among them along pathways called nadis.

In Mysticism, a Nadi (plural: Nadis) is an energy channel in which prana energy flows and may connect chakras. It is not accepted by mainstream science. The main nadis include *Shushumna*, *Ida* and *Pingala*.

Nadis are thought to carry a life force energy known as prana in Sanskrit, or Qi in Chinese based systems. They are also said to have an extrasensory function, playing a part in empathic and instinctive responses. Nadis are sometimes viewed as extending only to the skin of the body, but are often thought to extend to the boundary of the aura.

The Ida and Pingala nadis are often seen as referring to the two hemispheres of the brain. Pingala is the extroverted, solar nadi, and corresponds to the left hand side of the brain. Ida is the introverted, lunar nadi, and refers to the right hand side of the brain.

The two nadis are stimulated through the practice of pranayama (yoga breathing), which involves alternate breathing through left and right nostrils, which would alternately stimulate the left and right sides of the brain. The word nadi comes from the Sanskrit root nad meaning "channel", "stream", or "flow".

Within every living body, although on the subtle rather than the gross or physical level, there are said to be a series of energy fields or centers of consciousness, which in traditional Tantric teachings are called chakras = *"wheels"* or *padmas* = *"lotuses"*. They are said to be located either along, or just in front of, the backbone, even though they may express themselves externally at points along the front of the body (navel, heart, throat, etc). Associated with the chakras is a latent subtle energy, called *kundalini* in Shaktism, and *tumo* in Tibetan Buddhist Tantra.

Speculations and teachings concerning the chakras have occurred independently in the religious, spiritual, yogic,

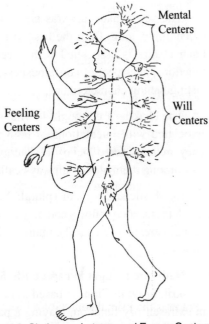

Fig. 4.2: Chakras or Lotuses and Energy Centers

and occult traditions of India, China, and the West. Although having certain basic points in common, these also differ in many details. So we have a number of different chakra-doctrines that have developed in different esoteric traditions to greater or lesser completeness.

The idea of the subtle vital force *(prana)* and the channels along which it flows *(nadis)* appear in the earliest *Upanishads* (7th-8th century B.C.). The heart was said to be the center of the 72,000 nadis or subtle channels, and the place into which the senses are withdrawn during sleep. As with many ancient civilisations (e.g. Egypt, Homeric Greece), the heart was also considered the seat of waking consciousness.

But it was only in the later Upanishads (the earlier of which were composed somewhere between the 2nd century B.C.E. and the 2nd century C.E.) that the first reference is made to basic Tantric concepts such as chakras, mantras, and so on.

The *Brahma-Upanishad* mentions the four "places" occupied by the purusha (soul): the navel, heart, throat, and head. Following common tradition, each place is characterised by a particular state of consciousness: the navel (or the eye) waking consciousness, the heart dreamless sleep, the throat dreaming, and the head the "fourth" or transcendent state. These four states, originally referred to in the *Mandukya Upanishad*, are identified with the gods Brahma, Vishnu, Rudra (a derivative of Shiva) and Akshara (the indestructible). The *Yogatattva Upanishad* speaks of the "five parts" of the body corresponding to the five great or cosmic elements: earth, water, fire, air, and space. Each element corresponds to a particular mantra - a "seed-vibration" or mystical syllable - and a particular deity. Emphasise is also given to *siddhis* (supernormal powers) that can be attained through mastery of yoga and of the different elements.

# What is Prana?

Prana is the primal source of all forms of energy and manifests itself in various frequencies. Your level of consciousness (awareness) determines the frequencies of prana you are capable of receiving and storing. One form of prana exists in the air, and one way we can retrieve it is through proper breathing (exercises).

Prana is equivalent to the force of "vitality." Vitality is radiated on all levels and manifests itself in the physical, emotional and mental realms. This force is NOT electricity, albeit in some ways it represents it.

One common description of the "vital force" (field) or "etheric body" is a silvery haze that extends a few inches beyond the skin. You can see this field under special conditions using ultra-violet light or your own eyes.

Fig. 4.3: 7 chakras (Refer plate 2 for Colour and labelled picture)

## How is Prana distributed in the body?

In the dense, physical body, the blood carries chemical material in a liquid solution; the red corpuscles taking oxygen to the tissue and bring back carbon dioxide from these and disposing of it. Well, the radiations in the "vital field" or "etheric body" absorb and carry "vitality" or "prana" from the other atmosphere and dispose of subtle waste matter in a similar manner.

Vitality action differs from electricity, light and heat. Vitality causes oscillation of the atoms as a whole, which is enormous compared to that of the atom. The "vitality force" comes to the atom from within, not from without. It enters the atom along with the force that holds the atom together. When this "vitality force" wells up within an atom, it gives it a power of attraction which immediately draws six (6) other atoms around it, thus creating a sub-atomic element called, "globules."

So "globules" are charged with the force of "prana." Globules are very good for you, btw. Under certain conditions, they can be seen dancing in the air as tiny points of brilliant light. They are also sunshine dependent for their power of manifestation. You won't see many under cloudy days. Perhaps this is why people are not as jovial or in a depressed or sluggish mood after being exposed to many cloudy and/or rainy days in a row.

In Hinduism and its spiritual systems of yoga and in some related eastern cultures, as well as in some segments of the New Age movement (and to some degree the distinctly different New Thought movement) a chakra is thought to be an energy node in the human body.

The word comes from the Sanskrit "chakra" meaning "wheel, circle", and sometimes also referring to the "wheel of life".

They function like receivers and transformers of the various forms of prana. Through the nadis, the chakras take in the vital energy and transform it into the frequencies needed by the various areas of the physical bodies for sustenance and development.

Each chakra is connected with one of the elements of earth, water, air ether and mind - mind being an instrument of consciousness. These elements are states of matter and NOT elements as we understand them in modern chemistry. They are equivalent to the terms: solid, liquid, fiery or gaseous, airy, and etheric - which are somewhat analogous to the physical, astral and mental planes and sub-planes.

Traditional writings say there are 88,000 chakras in the human body. Most are extremely small and play a minor role in your energy system. However, there are approximately 40 secondary chakras that are of significance; these are located in your spleen, the back of your neck, the palms of your hands and the soles of your feet. But for brevity and clarity purposes, in this we will only explore the seven primary chakras.

If we look down into the bell of a convoluted-type flower, we would get the general appearance of a chakra.

Fig. 4.4

The seven primary chakras are located along a central vertical axis of our spine and open toward the front of the body like a blossom. These circular energy centers are in constant motion, rotating, attracting energy, receiving or radiating.

At the center of each chakra, in its deepest point, is a stem-like channel that extends to the spine and merges with it, thus connecting the individual chakra with the sushumna (the most important energy channel) which ascends within the spine to the top of the head.

Fig. 4.5

Depending on the sex of the individual, the chakras rotate either clockwise or counter-clockwise. For instance, when a chakra in a man is rotating clockwise, the same chakra in a woman will rotate counter-clockwise and visa versa. This enables the energies of man and woman to compliment each other. Every clockwise rotation is primary male, which is in accordance with the Chinese teaching, Yang; and every counter-clockwise rotation is female, or Ying.

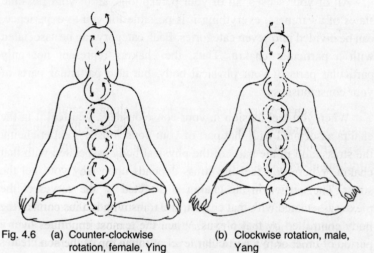

Fig. 4.6   (a) Counter-clockwise      (b) Clockwise rotation, male,
           rotation, female, Ying        Yang

It should be noted, the direction in which a chakra rotates varies from chakra to chakra. Each chakra rotates in a different direction, as these illustrations depict.

So, the chakras or *energy centers* function as pumps or valves, regulating the flow of energy through our energy system. The functioning of the chakras reflects decisions we make concerning how we choose to respond to conditions in our life. We open and close these valves when we decide what to think, and what to feel, and through which perceptual filter we choose to experience the world around us.

The chakras are not physical. They are aspects of consciousness in the same way that the auras are aspects of consciousness. The chakras are more dense than the auras, but not as dense as the physical body.

They interact with the physical body through two major vehicles, the endocrine system and the nervous system. Each of the seven chakras is associated with one of the seven endocrine glands, and also with a group of nerves called a plexus. Thus, each chakra can be associated with particular parts of the body and particular functions within the body controlled by that plexus or that endocrine gland associated with that chakra.

All of your senses, all of your perceptions, all of your possible states of awareness, everything it is possible for you to experience, can be divided into seven categories. Each category can be associated with a particular chakra. Thus, the chakras represent not only particular parts of your physical body, but also particular parts of your consciousness.

When you feel tension in your consciousness, you feel it in the chakra associated with that part of your consciousness experiencing the stress, and in the parts of the physical body associated with that chakra. Where you feel the stress depends upon why you feel the stress. The tension in the chakra is detected by the nerves of the plexus associated with that chakra, and transmitted to the parts of the body controlled by that plexus. When the tension continues over a period of time, or to a particular level of intensity, the person creates a symptom on the physical level.

The symptom speaks a language that reflects the idea that we each create our reality, and the metaphoric significance of the symptom becomes apparent when the symptom is described from that point of view. Thus, rather than saying, "I can't see," the person would describe it as keeping themselves from seeing something. "I can't walk," means the person has been keeping themselves from walking away from a situation in which they are unhappy. And so on.

The symptom serves to communicate to the person through their body what they had been doing to themselves in their consciousness. When the person changes something about their way of being, getting the message communicated by the symptom, the symptom has no further reason for being, and it can be released, according to whatever the person allows themselves to believe is possible.

*Anything can be healed. It's just a question of how to do it!*

Understanding the chakras allows you to understand the relationship between your consciousness and your body, and to thus see your body as a map of your consciousness. It gives you a better understanding of yourself and those around you.

Traditional Chinese medicine also relies on a similar model of the human body as an energy system.

The New Age movement has led to an increased interest in the West regarding chakras. Many in this movement point to a correspondence between the position and role of the Chakras, and those of the glands in the endocrine system. Some people in New Age also claim that other chakras, besides the above, exist - for instance, ear chakras.

*Chakrology* is a neologism sometimes employed by Alternative Medicine practitioners or esoteric philosophers for the study of chakras. There are many different chakrologies, some of them based on ancient Indian Hindu Tantric esoteric traditions, New Age interpretations, or Western occult analyses, as well as ancient Greek and Christian references. Croatian esoteric philosopher and physicist Arvan Harvat notes that it would be very difficult to develop a unified coherent chakra science that would integrate all the elements of the various present chakrologies.

So, to summarize, a chakra is a center of energy which has several functions. In addition to being 'representative' of a particular organ or group of organs, a chakra also controls our being on different levels and it links these two representative states.

The concept of chakra is very important in therapies such as reiki, meditation, yoga, therapeutic touch, aura, etc. Because of its wider application across a number of disciplines it is covered as a separate topic.

## How do chakra centers work?

We already said that each chakra is perpetually rotating. At the mouth of the chakra, a divine force from the higher world flows. Without this inrush of primary energy, the physical body could not exist.

The chakra centers are in constant operation in all of us. In the undeveloped person, they are usually in sluggish motion, just forming the necessary vortex for the force to enter, and not much more than that. However, in the more evolved person, they may be glowing and pulsating with living light so that an enormous amount of energy passes through them.

The divine energy that pours into each chakra from without sets up at right angles to itself secondary forces in an oscillating circular motion. Think of this like a magnet that produces a current around a coil at right angles to its axis.

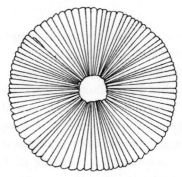

Fig. 4.7

After entering the vortex, the primary force radiates from it at right angles as straight lines, as though the center of the vortex was the hub of a wheel and the radiations of the primary force were the spokes.

The force of these spokes seems to bind the astral and etheric bodies together like grappling-hooks. The number of these spokes differs in each chakra, which determines the number of petals each chakra exhibits. This is why the chakras have been described in oriental books as resembling flowers.

Each of the secondary forces, which sweep around the saucer-shaped depressions, has its own wavelength and moves along large petals of various sizes. The number of petals is determined by the number of spokes in the wheel, and the secondary force weaves itself under and over the radiating currents of the primary force like a basket might be woven around the spokes of a wheel - the number of wavelengths being infinitesimal.

All the petals have a shimmering effect, like the mother-of-pearl, yet each has its own predominant colour. This silvery aspects is likened in Sanskrit works to the gleam of moonlight on the surface of the water.

## Why are colours associated with the chakras?

Each chakra contains all colour variations, although one colour always dominates. These colours correspond to the primary task of the chakra. Each globule that I spoke of earlier consists of seven (7) atoms. When these brilliant specks of light are drawn into the vortex of the 2nd (sacral or spleen) chakra, they are decomposed and break up into streams of different colours. As these seven (7) atoms are whirled around the vortex, each of the six spokes of the 2nd chakra seizes upon one of them so that all those charged with yellow flow along one spoke, those charged with green along another spoke, and so on, while the seventh atom disappears through the center of the vortex, or hub of the wheel. These rays then pass off in different directions, each ray destined to its special work in vitalization of the body.

It is important to note that the divisions of prana are not like what we normally see in the solar spectrum but resemble the arrangement of colours we see on the higher levels in the causal, mental and astral bodies.

For example, indigo is divided between the violet ray and the blue ray. Red is divided into two - rose red and dark red.

Consequently, the six atom radiants are: violet, blue, green, yellow, orange, and dark red, while the 7th, or rose-red atom passes down through the center of the vortex.

Vitality, therefore, is sevenfold in its constitution, but flowing through the body in five main streams. These five main streams are:

➢ The violet-blue ray

➢ the yellow ray

➢ the green ray

➢ The rose ray

➢ The orange-red ray

Fig. 4.8: Colour spectrum
(Refer Plate 3 for Colour picture)

So it should be no surprise that here is a certain correspondence between the colours of the streams (flow) of prana and the chakras. These streams are:

| (Prana) Colour | Chakra |
| --- | --- |
| Red | Root |
| Rose | Sacral (or Spleen) |
| Yellow (or gold) | Solar Plexus |
| Green | Heart |
| Light blue | Throat |
| Dark blue | Third Eye |
| Violet | Crown |

The body has seven basic body chakras and a number of minor chakras. These are from the lowest to the highest:

➢ The Root Chakra

➢ The Sexual Chakra

➢ The Personality Chakra

➢ The Heart Chakra

➢ The Expressive Chakra

➢ The Knowledge Chakra

➢ The Crown Chakra

Fig. 4.9

The number of major chakras does vary in some instances, e.g. Hindu yoga has six centers, but the greatest variation is in the minor chakras. In some regimes of therapy ten minor chakras are identified, and these are interconnected with the major chakras. A typical system could be:

> One in the arch of each foot, connected to the first and third chakras

> One in each knee joint, connected to the fifth and sixth chakras

> One in each palm, connected to the second, third and fourth

> Chakras one in each elbow, connected to the second and third chakras

> One below each shoulder, connected to the third and fifth chakras

## Primary Chakras

A distinction has to be made between primary and secondary chakras, as these are very often confused. The primary chakras are the inner chakras, i.e. the chakras as described by the original Tantra (essentially Yoga and/or Hindu traditions), which can only be accessed through yogic practice. These chakras are archetypal and do not have a form; the form they are represented as in Tantric literature is stylized and symbolic. Nor do they have a precise location. They are associated with specific correspondences including mantric (from mantra) vibrations, elements, gods, etc.

The primary chakras are represented in an up-down vertical axis (the microcosmic "Mount Meru" – world mountain), and are polarized according to Shiva (Pure Unmanifest Consciousness, The Godhead) and Shakti (the Female power of manifestation). Shakti is represented by the Kundalini energy at the base of the spine, or more strictly speaking, in the Muladhara chakra (which as with all the Primary Chakras does not have a strict physical location). Shiva is located in the crown chakra (Saharsrara) at the crown above the head.

This vertical polarization represents the major planes of existence: Earthly, and Spiritual or Cosmic.

As microcosmic archetypes the primary chakras can be equated with the ten Sefirot of Kabbalah, which are arranged, significantly, in seven rows. Various attempts have been made to equate the two, but none appear to be completely satisfactory.

## The 7 Primary Chakras

| Name | Number | Associated with |
|---|---|---|
| Muladhara | Chakra one | Survival |
| Svadhisthana | Chakra two | Emotions and sexuality |
| Manipura (Nabhi) | Chakra three | Power and will |
| Anahata | Chakra four | Love and balance |
| Vishudda | Chakra five | Communication and creativity |
| Agnya (Ajna) | Chakra six | Intuition and imagination |
| Sahasrara | Chakra seven | Knowledge and understanding |

## Secondary Chakras

The secondary chakras are the chakras described by Theosophy, the New Age movement, and in general are the ones widely seen in Western literature and schools. Unlike the archetypal Primary chakras they have a specific form (usually described as vortexes of energy), colour and a specific precise location in the Auric body (the realm of the physical body and its aura). These Primary chakras are Etheric (body whose realm & density lies between that of the astral and physical bodies) and pertain to the Outer Being, which includes not only the ordinary everyday consciousness but even psychic, occult and many transpersonal and mystic states.

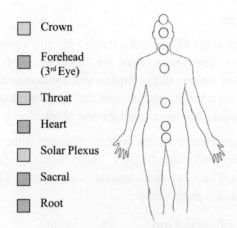

Crown

Forehead
(3rd Eye)

Throat

Heart

Solar Plexus

Sacral

Root

Fig. 4.10: Chakras centers

For the sake of clarity, since these two systems APPEAR to be similar in "location" and "number of chakras", the following table illustrates the rough equivalence of the two.

Please remember that the two systems refer to entirely different philosophies, objectives and methods, so they are not really "equivalent".

| rear chakras (ascending channel) SECONDARY | central chakras (inner being) PRIMARY | front chakras (descending channel) SECONDARY |
|---|---|---|
| Crown | Sahasrara | Crown |
| Back of Head | Ajna | Upper Forehead/ 3rd eye |
| Base of Neck | Vishuddha | Throat / Thymic |
| Shoulder Blades | Anahata | Heart |
| Diaphragmatic | Manipura | Solar Plexus |
| Door of Life | - | Navel |
| Sacral | Svadhisthana | Pubic / Genitals |
| Coccygeal | Muladhara | Base |

As you can see, it is easy to "equate" the two systems, believing that just the names of the Chakras change, but they are quite different in philosophy, objectives and methods of accessing or "opening" them.

## Chakra System

The Chakra system is the closest thing that we have to a map of our own consciousness. Sometimes called the "Rainbow Bridge", this system is our way of making things happen and communicating with the divine. There is no hard scientific proof that the chakras exist, but as a theoretical model, they have stood the test of time.

There are seven chakras in the system. Starting at the bottom, they are the Root (1st), Sacral (2nd), Solar Plexus (3rd), Heart (4th), Throat (5th), Third Eye (6th), and the Crown (7th). There are primarily interpreted in three ways:

### 1. A process of evolution

With this system we can observe our progress through this life. First, we explore the physical body (1st chakra). Then we find our emotions (2nd chakra). And third, we form our own mental image of the world (3rd chakra). These three things represent the upward flow of energy from the bottom three chakras. The upper three chakras represent our spiritual centers with the Heart (4th chakra) being the bridge between the physical and the spiritual. As a species we are now experiencing the evolution of the Heart (4th chakra), which will give a conscious way to open the top three chakras.

### 2. Energy transformation

Although healing with energy is well documented, it still confuses scientists trying to explain it. For some scientists, it may seem absurd for subtle energy of the body to be changed by love or prayer. The prayer or love enters the top chakras and works its way down to the bottom chakras to allow physical change. This may be a bit far fetched for some, but consider that each chakra is in line with the respective endocrine gland:

*Chakra 1 (Root) - Adrenal gland*
*Chakra 2 (Sacral) - Gonads/Ovaries*
*Chakra 3 (Solar Plexus/Navel) - Spleen/Pancreas*
*Chakra 4 (Heart) - Thymus*

*Chakra 5 (Throat) - Thyroid gland*
*Chakra 6 (Third Eye) - Pituitary gland*
*Chakra 7 (Crown) - Pineal gland*

## 3. Esoteric instruction

Some say that in physical reality, the chakras do not exist. Some feel that they are merely focal points for our concentration, gateways to other states of being if you will. The lower three chakras relate to the physical world, the top three relate to the spiritual world. As we move up the system from the bottom, the vibration increases.

A person centerd in the lower chakras will vibrate at a lower rate than those centerd higher in the system.

The chakra system can been viewed as a *"seven-levelled philosophical model of the universe."* The seven chakras (Sanskrit for wheels or disks) are wheels of bio-energetic activity radiating from nerve ganglia (clusters) that start at the base of the spine and continue on to the crown of the head. Although the energy of the chakras can be monitored, they have no mass or substance of their own. Each individual chakra does, however, have a general location. These locations are as follows:

| Name | Number | Element | Location | Associated with |
|------|--------|---------|----------|-----------------|
| Muladhara | Chakra one | (earth) | Base of spine | *Survival.* |
| Svadhisthana | Chakra two | (water) | Lower abdomen | *Emotions and sexuality.* |
| Manipura (Nabhi) | Chakra three | (fire) | Solar plexus | Power and will. |
| Anahata | Chakra four | (air) | Just over the sternum (Heart) | *Love and balance.* |
| Vishudda | Chakra five | (sound) | Throat | Communication and creativity. |
| Agnya (Ajna) | Chakra six | (light) | Center of forehead (brow) | *Intuition and imagination.* |
| Sahasrara | Chakra seven | (thought) | Top of head | Knowledge and understanding. |

It is clear now that the lower chakras are more dense and material, while the higher chakras are more "free" and conceptual. It is an eastern belief that this is because they are closer to their source. Beyond the crown is Shiva, the male principle, believed to symbolize pure consciousness and bliss. Beyond the root is Shakti, the female principle, the mother of the universe and creation itself (herself?). By coming together in union, Shiva can descend upon Shakti and bring Divine Consciousness into the universe while Shakti brings form to pure consciousness.

This can be seen in mundane life as well:

*Ideas (chakra 7) become **visualized** (chakra 6) and then **shared** with others verbally or **written down** (chakra 5). **The love** of the idea (chakra 4) brings one to invest their will and energy into its **creation** (chakra 3). The **passion/need** (chakra 2) to finish this act of creation urges one to provide it **form** (chakra 1) and thus finish the process.*

This is a transfer of ideas into form the manifesting current. Consequently, the transfer of form into ideas can be thought of as the liberating current. These two forces are constantly running through the body and connecting the chakras.

Chapter 5

# The 7 Chakras

The spine and the human energy field contain chakras, or energy centers, that vibrate at different frequencies. Each chakra presents us with the opportunity to establish a root relationship and to satisfy a deep soul desire. Each frequency holds the gift of a certain power, which enhances our human experience on Planet Earth. As we tune into this power, we are internally empowered to deal with the specific life challenges of that energy center or chakra and as a consequence to live more whole, meaningful and fulfilling lives.

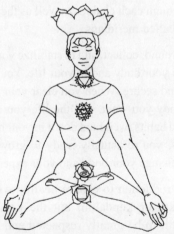

Fig. 5.1: Positions of 7 chakras

Energy flows from the Crown Chakra through to all the major chakras. Earth energy also flows, beginning in the Root Chakra and rising through the other energy centers. You can boost your energy quickly, by focusing on each one in turn, and breathing "into" each daily. Visualize the corresponding colour as you do this, and focus on the body areas and domains governed by each chakra in turn. Try sounding the mantra that relates to each.

| Chakra | Literal Translation | Body Center | bija mantra | "Element" |
|--------|--------------------|-----------|------------|-----------|
| Sahasrara | "thousand-spoked wheel" | Crown | '!' | 'Spirit' |
| Ajna | "command wheel" | Third-eye | OM | Manas(?) |
| Vishuddha | "pure wheel" | Throat | HAM | "Akasha" |
| Anahata | "wheel of the unstruck sound" | Heart | YAM | Air |
| Manipura | "wheel of the jewelled city" | Solar-plexus | RAM | Fire |
| Svadhisthana | "wheel of the self-base" | Navel | VAM | Water |
| Muladhara | "root-foundation wheel" | Base | LAM | Earth |

Mantras work like an ultrasound or sine wave to increase the flow of energy through each chakra, as well as the rest of your body's energy channels, called meridians.

Learning to ground, collect, and to stabilize your energy will make a big difference in your body and in your life. You will feel anchored, connected, safe, and secure. When you clear your energy, you're able to manifest the body you want, and the life you dream of. If you're feeling stuck in old habits, weighted down in your body, and filled with negative emotions, you're actually ready to grow! When you direct your energy, you change your body and your experience of life.

This short introduction to chakra healing will never do justice to the earth chakra or kundalini, but the beginning practitioner should know that it to be greatly respected and can be gone to (in conjunction with the crown by placing the right hand on the skull and left on the tailbone region to balance energy or move energy through the entire system.

Let's learn a little bit more about each Tantra Chakra now.

# Root Chakra
## Connect to Body and Earth

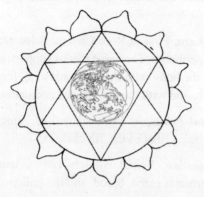

## Foundation

This is the source of strength and is essential for proper development. The other centers of energy rely upon the root chakra to perform properly. Disorders within the root chakras may result in mental problems (e.g. aggression, confusion) or physical symptoms (e.g. of the intestines, excretory systems, or bones).

*The earth chakra (muladhara)* is the most important chakra in hatha yoga, It is where the kundalini lies dormant and it is where the prana and apana are to be balanced for the energy (kundalini) to flow in the central column (sushumna) . This should not be interpreted as just some mystical gibberish, but yet the words certainly are symbolic of a very powerful energetic. Again once flow is reached in the sushumna it is neither left nor right, nor up nor down (flow is in both directions simultaneously). Again the muladhara and sahasrara chakras are the two most important energetic centers while the sushumna is the most important psychic nerve (that connects them) directly. Physically this area is associated with the perineum, tailbone, glands of Luska, and pelvic diaphragm.

This area is often congested so elongating smoothing and softening passes with the hands up and down over this area can often be of value. The muladhara is the integrative physical center of the body and its support center.

Located at the base of the spine, it contains the primary 8 cells that have all of the knowledge of creation and remain the only cells in your body that do not change in your lifetime. It grounds us in the physical world.

*The Muladhara*, First or Root Chakra, is located at the base of the spine, at the perineum. The name means support, or foundation. It is associated, in the body with the large intestine, feet and legs, with the element earth, and with the colours red and maroon.

*Fundamental Principle*: Physical will of being as opposed to spiritual will of being (that of the 7th chakra).

*Body Association*: Spinal column, bones, teeth, nails, anus, rectum, colon, prostate gland, blood, and the building of cells.

*Glands*: Suprarenal glands (which produce adrenalin and influence the temperature balance of the body).

*Human Challenge and Gift*: to feel safe and secure in the physical plane, to manifest to meet our basic needs.

*Soul Desire*: To feel nurtured and nourished, to experience belonging to the whole.

*Primal Relationship*: With physical reality, the Earth, natural forces, body, feeling, sensations.

Fig. 5.2: 1st Chakra - Base/perineum, red, Earth, survival, grounding, stillness, elephant

| Root or Base Chakra | |
|---|---|
| Colour Association | Red |
| Key words | Grounding, security, basic needs |
| Force | Gravity |
| Verb | I have |
| Sanskrit Name | Muladhara |
| Location | Base of spine, coccyx |
| Lesson | Survival–The right to exist. Deals with tasks related to the material and physical world. Ability to stand up for oneself and security issues. |
| Imbalances | Anaemia, fatigue, lower back pain, sciatica, depression. Frequent colds or cold hands and cold feet. Constipation, obesity, lower back pain, haemorrhoids |
| Animal | Elephant |
| Element | Earth |
| Celestial Body | Saturn |
| Sense | Smell |
| Food | Protein |
| Root Stimulants | Physical exercise and restful sleeps, gardening, pottery and clay. Red food & drink. Red gemstones, red clothing, bathing in red, etc. Using red oils such as ylang or sandalwood essential oils. |

## Purpose and Function

The 1st chakra (Root Chakra) is located between the anus and the genitals. It is connected with the coccyx and opens downward. It connects us to the physical world and lets the earthly energy enter our system. When it is open, we fully accept life on earth and enjoy the physical existence it provides. We act in harmony with the earthly forces and we learn from them. It also provides us with the necessary energy for creative self-expression and lends us the power to achieve. Our sexuality as a physical function and a means of begetting children also reign in the Root Chakra.

The Root Chakra is the source of the life force and forms the vital foundation for all the higher chakras. Here, the inexhaustible supply of kundalini energy is awakened. The sushumna, ida and pingala (the three main energy channels of the human body) begin in this chakra.

The Root Chakra is the true seat of the collective unconscious. Through this chakra, the stored knowledge of the collective unconscious becomes accessible. This chakra should always function in harmony with the seventh chakra in order to maintain our inner balance.

## Harmonious Functioning

If your Root Chakra is open and functioning harmoniously, you will experience a deep, personal relationship with Earth and earthly life forms (Nature). You are rooted in life and your life is filled with satisfaction, stability and inner strength. Your actions are guided by the desire to be creatively active in shaping life on planet Earth. You perceive the earth as a shelter and secure place. It provides you with all your physical, psychological and emotional needs. You are truly grateful for life on earth.

## Disharmonious Functioning

If your Root Chakra is unbalanced or malfunctioning, your thoughts and actions primarily revolve around material possessions and security, as well as your over indulgence in sensual pleasures such as, good (exotic) foods, alcohol, sex, etc. You want your desires to manifest without consideration of the consequences. Your inability to let go of these tendencies often manifest themselves in the form of constipation and gaining weight, as in overweight.

Your actions revolve around satisfying your personal needs and you unconsciously overlook or ignore the needs of others as well as your own (i.e. good health, sufficient rest and a balanced and harmonious life.) In the extreme, if you are challenged by people or situations, you become easily irritated, upset, aggressive, and you may have a tendency to violently enforce your will upon others. These feelings of rage, anger and violence are actually a defence mechanism which indicate a lack of trust -- it's a fear of losing that which provides you with security and a feeling of well-being, or your inability to gain it in the first place.

If your Root Chakra is blocked or closed, you will lack physical and emotional stamina. A lot of things in life worry you. You are filled with feelings of uncertainty. You lack the power to achieve. Often, you see life on earth as a burden. For you, life on earth is NOT a pleasure. Most of the time you long for an easier, more pleasant and less strenuous way of life.

If you have developed your higher chakras and neglected your lower ones, you may feel that you don't belong on the earth. If your Sacral (2nd) Chakra and your Solar Plexus (3rd) Chakra are also blocked, anorexia may result.

*One centerd in this chakra needs, above all, to feel truly safe. Insecurity may be a problem if needs are not met.*

# Sex Chakra
Unleash, freedom

## Sweetness

This is highly influential and governs sensual and sexual factors, the means whereby experiences are felt and registered. Blockages result in a variety of phobias or conditions such as a fear of being touched, a general incomprehension or an obsessive cleanliness. Physical manifestations may include being prone to infections, or problems with the kidneys/bladder or lymphatic system.

Located just beneath the navel and related to our sexual and reproductive capacity. Blockage manifests as emotional problems or sexual guilt.

*The second chakra (water chakra) called the swadhistana chakra* can suffer from deficiency or blocked energy flow through it (functional flow). The water chakra is the energy vortex that reflects the health of our procreative function on the physical level (something that this society generally associates with sin and danger), but on an emotional/energetic, and mental level it represents how we interact with all our relations -- how we engage and have a two way intercourse (communication and flow) with other beings and things. If it is blocked or toxic then these functions become imbalanced. For example some people who have blocked second chakra energetic (water chakra) compensate by neurotic talking, over eating, or excessive sublimation/discharge elsewhere. Often because the energy may be blocked at the water chakra then discharging this energy there in excessive sex or in urination problems sometimes result although the actual energetic of all these functions are the result of manifold interactions.

When it is deficient in energy there is deficiency in the sexual, generative, procreative, and creative urges. This is a motive force chakra where innate evolutionary energies are expressed and generative and regenerative energies are stored and expressed. In illness where these flows are damned up or restricted. Here resides our connection with fluid flow, the sea, change, shape shifting, seminal and creative ideas, imagination, creative inspiration, instinct, and spontaneity.

When sexual disturbances exist many people mistakenly suggest that there is too much energy flowing in the chakra, but what really is happening is that the energy is congested, dammed up/blocked, stepped on, abused, inhibited from flowing either below or above, and hence it "appears" to want to come "out" and be discharged (or there is fear and shame associated in its expression). Because of inhibitory influences of unnatural belief systems, social mores, self censure, guilt, alien religions, and other artificial and non-body positive external influences a conflict between natural and spontaneous creative/ procreative expression becomes reinforced establishing a body/mind discordance, tension, conflict, and war which is an energetic source of much mental disturbances, social crime, violence, and physical dis-ease.

In the healthy body/mind the energy at the water chakra should be constantly streaming here without fear of attracting sexual negative notice from others (or guilt). If the center is dead, intuitive and instinctual senses are diminished. Women and men who have "sex appeal" often have vital first three chakras, but also in order to avoid sexual attention or condemnation many women and men turn off this center in order to avoid the attention of others often in fear or shame. This is a particularly common and strong, yet not widely recognized dynamic.

In most cases where there is a tendency toward paranoia and alienation accompanied by tightness in the pelvis and sacrum, the energy is blocked going downward from the swadhistana, while in cases of lack of metabolic process, will power, or ability to manage one's own affairs the energy is blocked going upward (into the manipura chakra). If the energy is blocked in both directions at the same time, there almost always exists a deficiency where a one way blockage can create a distorted shunt manifesting in what may appear as an over stimulation.

Since sex is a powerful issue in modern life, many clients (those who are numbed out or constricted in the swadhistana area will be embarrassed to allow energy to flow here and will resist energetic streaming. If such occurs the therapist may try streaming the energy between the muladhara (pelvic diaphragm floor) THROUGH the swadhistana to the manipura (at the lumbar region and above so that the energy does not get stuck in the sexual region. Once the client realizes that the energy can be energized but not locked into that area (obsessed) but made to flow through it without congestion then further cooperation in release of this area will be more easily accomplished. This liberated energy can be used for healing in the swadhistana, muladhara, or brought to the manipura chakra above for further balance and catalyzation of flow . This area thus must be honoured with sensitivity and gentleness while the therapist must be capable of thoroughly moving through any personal sexual feelings that may become stimulated.

Strongly associated with not only the gonads, prostate/ovaries, bladder, sacrum, and lower back. This center resonates in a simple harmonic order with the pituitary (ajna chakra or third eye) just as the muladhara has a special resonance with the sahasrara. Although this is the water chakra (usually white in colour), the kidneys and adrenals being higher up are usually associated with the next center, the manipura chakra which is characterized by the fire element.

**The Swadisthana** or Sex Chakra is located at the sacrum - the pelvic area between pubis and navel. Its name means "abode of the vital force" or "dwelling place of the self. It is associated, in the body with the genitals, reproductive organs, and bladder, with the element water, and the colour orange.

**Human Challenge and Gift**: To bond and connect with others without losing our identity.

**Soul Desire**: To freely expand, to effortlessly create.

**Fundamental Principle**. Creative reproduction of being.

**Body Association**: Pelvic girdle, kidneys, bladder, and all liquids, such as, blood, lymph, gastric juice, sperm and regulation of the female cycle.

**Glands**: Prostate, gonads, ovaries, testicles.

**Primal Relationship**: With other human beings, emotions and emotional body, inner child, wild man or wild woman.

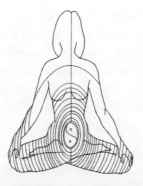

Fig. 5.3: 2nd Chakra - Lower abdomen, orange, water, emotions, sexuality, desire, tears, crocodile, moon

| Spleen Chakra | |
| --- | --- |
| Colour Association | Orange |
| Key note | Creativity, sexuality, desire |
| Force | Magnetism |
| Verb | I feel |
| Sanskrit Name | Svadisthana |
| Location | Below navel, lower abdomen |
| Lesson | Feelings—The right to feel. Connected to our sensing abilities and issues related to feelings. Ability to be social and intimacy issues |
| Imbalances | Eating disorders. Alcohol and drug abuse. Depression. Low back pain. Asthma or allergies. Candida & yeast infections. Urinary problems. Sensuality issues as well as impotence and frigidity |
| Animal | Crocodile |
| Element | Water |
| Celestial body | Moon |
| Food | Liquids |
| Sense | Taste |
| Spleen Stimulants | Hot aromatic baths, water aerobics, massage. Embracing sensation (such as different food tastes). Orange food & drink. Orange gemstones and orange clothing. Using orange oils such as melissa or orange essential oils |

## Purpose and Function

The 2nd chakra (Sacral Chakra) is located above the genitals. It is connected with the sacrum and opens towards the front. We fertilize and receive the energies that permeate all of nature through the Sacral Chakra. The male reproductive organs as well as the impulse to procreate new life is influenced by this chakra.

Water cleanses and purifies. It dissolves and washes away the blockages that obstruct its vital flow. Albeit the kidneys and bladder accomplish this on the physical plane, on the spiritual plane the cleansing and purification process manifests itself in the form of free-flowing feelings. We look at life as something primordial and new, and our interpersonal relationships with the opposite sex are particularly influenced by the condition of the Sacral Chakra.

## Harmonious Functioning

An open and harmoniously functioning Sacral Chakra allows you to open yourself towards others, especially the opposite sex. Your sexual union with your lover (partner) blossoms into the dance of creation. You feel the flow of the male and female energies streaming through your body, soul and mind.

## Disharmonious Functioning

The Sacral Chakra comes alive during puberty. This is when a malfunctioning Sacral Chakra often originates. The awakening of sexual energies causes a state of uncertainty within you. Parents and educators rarely teach people how to handle these energies. During your early infancy, there may have been a lack of tenderness and bodily contact, which may later lead to the rejection of sexuality. As a result, you are unable to experience the uninhibited expression of your creative sexual potential and these uninhibited energies may express themselves in the form of excessive sexual fantasies or suppressed desires. You may also see sex as a drug. What you need to understand is that your creative sexuality has just been misdirected. These actions breed uncertainty and sexual tension between the sexes.

In most cases, inadequate functioning of the Sacral Chakra can be traced back to childhood and infancy. Your parents probably withheld their own sensuality and sexuality. Additionally, you probably had a lack of sensual stimulation in the form of touching, caresses, tenderness and affection. Consequently, you suppressed your feelings and withdrew your antennas, so to speak, turning off these sensual messages. Then, during puberty, you may have blocked off your developing sexual energies completely. This suppression results in a lack of self-esteem, emotional paralysis and sexual coldness. Life in this light seems dreary and you may feel life is not worth living. These feelings often amplify teenagers' tendencies to commit suicide.

*One centerd in this chakra needs the freedom to be creative. They may indulge a little much in their desires.*

# Navel Chakra    Solar Plexus Chakra

Come Alive    **or**    Deepen

## Lustrous Gem

It's the *'personality'* chakra. It is also called the solar plexus chakra, this is the power center and focus of personal freedom or, conversely, feelings of guilt. Mental consequences of a blockage might be anxiety about how others perceive you, envy or selfish greed. Physically there could be digestive disorders, liver and gall bladder problems or disorders of the pancreas.

. *The Fire Chakra (Manipura Chakra)* is the integrative energy center of the body has a special primary resonance, this time with the throat chakra (vishuddi). This is the center for individual strength, vitality, self empowerment, ability to get things done, will power, concentration, action (fire), metabolism, and the like. If the linear pathway is blocked/congested (up or down) then excess fire or depleted dysfunction may similarly occur. It is too often ignored because on a physical level it may represent our gastric fire or ability to digest food and hence is relegated to the gastrointestinal tract which is normally a subject (especially the lower end) that is considered "low" and distasteful. As a result our energy is often ignored and people suffer from lack of energy diseases, gastrointestinal illnesses, costiveness, greed, lack of ability to digest new ideas, allergies, and the like.

In this sense the swadhistana chakra is the center of energetic well being, personal physical strength, and self confidence, it being the place where the fuel is burned to drive the physical engines of the neuro-physiological organism. Here in the manipura chakra the added fire, heat, or energy required to cook the broth, heat the cauldron, distill the elixir, and/or bubble over into the air (heart) chakra (called the *anahata* chakra in Sanskrit).

**The Manipuraka** or Navel Chakra is located some 2-3 inches below the navel. It's name means *"jewel of the lotus" or "lustrous gem"*.

It is associated, in the body with the small intestine, kidneys, adrenals, pancreas, gallbladder, liver, with the element fire, and the colour yellow.

**Human Challenge and Gift**: To connect with our internal source power and energy; to transmute the energy of the emotions into soulful passion for life i.e. fear into love, anger into action, sadness into surrender and bliss.

**Soul Desire**: To ignite, connect with and focus physical energy; to experience the depth of emotions and transmute them into passion and devotion; to activate the soul.

Fig. 5.4: 3rd Chakra - Solar plexus, yellow, fire, will, power, anger, joy, laughter, ram, sun

**Primal Relationship**: With internal source of power, identity, status; with our soul and emotional body.

**Fundamental Principle**: Shaping of things.

**Body Association**: Lower back, abdomen, digestive system, stomach, liver, spleen, gallbladder, autonomic nervous system.

**Glands**: Pancreas, which plays an important role in the digestion of food and the secretion of insulin.

| Solar Plexus Chakra | |
|---|---|
| **Colour Association** | Yellow |
| **Key words** | Power, will |
| **Verb** | I do, I can |
| **Force** | Combustion |
| **Sanskrit Name** | Manipura |
| **Location** | Above the navel, stomach area |
| **Lesson** | Personal power–The right to think. Balance of intellect, self-confidence and ego power. Ability to have self-control and humour |

| Imbalances | Digestive problems, ulcers, diabetes, hypoglycaemia, constipation. Nervousness, toxicity, parasites, colitis, poor memory |
|---|---|
| Animal | Gout |
| Element | Fire |
| Celestial body | Sun |
| Sense | Sight |
| Food | Carbohydrates |
| Solar Plexus Stimulants | Taking classes, reading informative books, doing mind puzzles. Sunshine. Detoxication programs. Yellow food & drink. Yellow gemstones and yellow clothing. Using yellow oils such as lemon or rosemary essential oils |

## Purpose and Function

The 3rd chakra (Solar Plexus Chakra) is located about two fingers above the navel and opens towards the front. Its functions are highly complex. It represents our sun and our power center. We absorb the solar energy through the Solar Plexus, which nurtures our ethereal body, energizing and maintaining our physical body. Also, our emotional energy radiates from here.

The foundation of our personality is represented through the Solar Plexus Chakra. Our social identity and our desire to confirm it by personal assertion, our will to achieve, our striving for power, and our adaptation to social patterns all are influenced by the Solar Plexus Chakra.

The most important task of the Solar Plexus Chakra is to purify the desires and wishes of the lower chakras (Sacral and Root). To consciously control and use the creative energy of these lower chakras and allow the spiritual higher chakras to manifest in the material world is the greatest possible fullfilment.

The Solar Plexus is directly connected to our astral (emotional) body, which is the center of our wishes and desires. *If we accept and integrate our feelings, wishes and experiences in our lives, this will help our Solar Plexus relax and open up,* thus increasing our inner light and illuminating our situation in life.

Our moods are influenced by the amount of light we permit to shine within us. When the Solar Plexus Chakra is opened, we feel enlightened, full of joy, and an inner richness. If it is blocked, closed or disturbed, we feel gloomy and unbalanced, etc. It is important to note that we also PROJECT the same moods and sensations into the world (environment) around us. Life therefore may seem either bright or dark to us. It is the amount of light within us that determines the clearness of our vision and the quality of what we see.

We also directly perceive the vibrations of other people through the Solar Plexus and react accordingly. If we are confronted with negative vibrations, this chakra warns us. You've heard the saying, "I've got a gut feeling." This is your Solar Plexus talking to you.

## Harmonious Functioning

You feel peace and an inner harmony with your Self, life in general, and your place in the world. You have accepted yourself completely, and you respect the feelings and character traits of others. You also accept your feelings, wishes and experiences in life. You see them in the "right light." Your feelings, wishes and experiences are integrated in such a way that lead to wholeness of being.

As an additional bonus, if your Third Eye Chakra (6th chakra) and your Crown Chakra (7th chakra) are also open, you can recognize that all visible matter consists of varying degrees of light vibrations. Since all visible matter is light, when these chakras are functioning in harmony with each other, your wishes are fulfilled spontaneously. You are connected to the energy of light in all things, and therefore, you attract everything you are in search of to yourself.

## Disharmonious Functioning

When your Solar Plexus Chakra is malfunctioning, you want to manipulate everything in accordance with your own wishes and desires; you want to control your inner and outer worlds and conquer and exercise power. An inner restlessness and discontent drives you. You develop an enormous urge to keep active and busy. This urge is your way of covering up your persistent feelings of inadequacy and shortcomings. You just can't let go and relax. You need to understand that material wealth and recognition cannot provide you with true, long-term happiness.

Acceptance and material well-being are of primary importance for you. Your true emotions are all blocked, therefore, you are unable to express them. You get upset easily. Your irritation and agitation are an expression of all the anger you have swallowed over a long period of time. You feel dejected and discouraged. You see obstacles everywhere. You believe these obstacles are preventing you from fulfilling your desires. When faced with a difficult situation, you may feel queasy and uncertain, or you may get so nervous your actions become haphazard and disorganized. You want to hide from and avoid all new challenges in life. Your perception of life is not good. You see unhappy endings everywhere you turn.

*One centerd in this chakra has great will. They need to achieve and make something in this world. They hold the power of manipulation for inspiration.*

# Heart Chakra
## Clarity and Purity

## Unstruck

*The heart chakra* controls self-acceptance and by extension everyone else around us. Blockages may result in attitudes such as selfishness or emotional blackmail. Physical manifestations could be disorders of the lungs and heart, and circulatory problems.

The Anahatha or Heart Chakra is located at the heart. Its name means unstuck, fresh, clean unhurt.

It is associated, in the body with the heart, hands, arms and thymus gland, with the element air and the colours green, pink, and rose.

**Human Challenge and Gift**: To open our hearts to the nonjudgmental, detached vibration of universal love.

**Soul Desire**: To experience unity, devotion, reverence for life, unattached bonding.

**Primal Relationship**: With higher spiritual power, our own heart and the hearts of others, the pulse that unites us with the universe.

**Fundamental Principle**: Devotion, self-abandonment.

**Body Association**: Heart, upper back, thorax and thoracic cavity, lower lungs, the blood and circulatory system and the skin.

**Gland**: Thymus, which regulates and controls the lymphatic system.

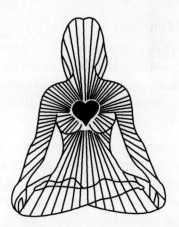

Fig. 5.5: 4th Chakra - Heart, green, air, love, balance, compassion, antelope

| Throat Chakra | |
|---|---|
| **Colour Association** | Mainly Blue but also Green, Pink, and sometimes Gold |
| **Key notes** | Love, compassion |
| **Verb** | I love |
| **Force** | Equilibrium |
| **Sanskrit Name** | Visuddha |
| **Location** | Throat region |
| **Lesson** | Relationships–The right to speak. Learning to express oneself and one's beliefs (truthful expression). Ability to trust. Loyalty. Organization and planning |
| **Imbalances** | Thyroid imbalances, swollen glands. Fevers and flu. Infections. Mouth, jaw, tongue, neck and shoulders problems. Hyperactivity. Hormonal disorders such as PMS, mood swings, bloating and menopause |
| **Animal** | Antelope or Dove |
| **Element** | Air |
| **Celestial body** | Venus |
| **Sense** | Touch |
| **Food** | Vegetables |
| **Throat Stimulants** | Singing (in the shower), poetry, stamp or art collecting. Meaningful conversations. Blue food & drink. Blue gemstones and blue clothing. Using blue oils such as chamomile or geranium essential oils |

## Purpose and Function

The 4th chakra (Heart Chakra) is located in the center of the breast at the height of your heart and opens toward the front. It is the center of the entire chakra system and connects the LOWER (Physical & Emotional Centers) to the three HIGHER (Mental & Spiritual Centers.)

The Heart Chakra is a very important chakra. With the Heart Chakra we find the capability to empathize and sympathize with others. We attune ourselves with the cosmic vibrations and perceive the beauty in nature, music, visual arts and poetry. Here, all images, words and sounds are transformed into feelings.

All yearning for deep intimate contact, oneness, harmony, love, even sorrow, pain, fear of separation or loss of love is expressed through the Heart Chakra. When completely opened, it forms the center of true "unconditional" love.

When this "unconditional" love is connected with the higher chakras, it transforms itself into Bhakti, the Divine Love, which guides us to unity with this Divine Heart of all things in the universe. En-route toward this goal, our heart must learn to love, understand and accept ourselves (personality) which is the prerequisite to saying "yes" to others and life in general. All our experiences, wishes and emotions have a much deeper sense and purpose, which guide us to a loving acceptance that all feelings and expressions of life originate from the longing for love.

With every negation and rejection, we regenerate separation and negativity, whereas a positive and loving acceptance (a conscious "yes") produces vibrations which neutralize (kill, so to speak) negative thoughts and feelings. Simply put, you can neutralize those intense feelings of grief, anger or despair with your loving, unbiased and undivided attention -- positive thoughts and feelings.

With our Heart Chakra, we possess a great potential for healing others as well as ourselves. If you suffer from pain or illness, send the afflicted organ or area of your body your loving attention and it will help and accelerate the recuperation period enormously. If we can learn to love from the depths of our own heart and fully accept our entire personality, an opened Heart Chakra can have a spontaneous healing or transforming influence on ourselves and others.

The Heart Chakra radiates colours of green, pink, and sometimes gold. Green is the colour of healing and sympathy and harmony. If an enlightened person (i.e. someone who can see human auras) perceives a clear, light-green in a person's heart chakra, this would indicate a well-developed capability to heal, while a golden aura mixed with pink would show a person who lives in pure and selfless love of the Divine.

Within the Heart Chakra is the deepest and most vivid feelings of love. It also plays an important role in refining the perception of an open Third Eye, and it is for this reason that the spiritual schools in the East concentrate particularly on the opening of the Heart Chakra.

## Harmonious Functioning

Working in harmony with all the other chakras, a completely open Heart Chakra can change the world around you and unite, reconcile, or even heal the person within your surroundings. Your entire being radiates natural warmth, sincerity and happiness. These wondrous energies open the hearts of the people around you, inspiring confidence and creating joy among them. A great compassion and willingness to help others comes perfectly natural to you.

You love for love's sake. You are motivated by the joy of giving and do not expect to gain anything in return. Your heart is in everything you do. You "unconditionally" love all!

Through this wisdom, you view the world and personal experiences in a new light. You no longer look at life from a distance and think that it has nothing to do with you. You see all life as part of your own life and that "life" in its purest and most original form really signifies an everlasting expression of Divine Love and bliss. All is love!

## Disharmonious Functioning

A malfunctioning Heart Chakra may express itself in various ways. You may want to always be there for others and give freely, but consciously, you may want/expect recognition in return for all the love you give them. Then, if your efforts are not sufficiently appreciated, you may feel deeply disappointed.

You may also feel that you are strong and powerful enough to give away some of your strength but incapable of accepting the love that others may want to give you. In this way, you are unable to open yourself to receiving the love of others. Emotions aligned with tenderness and softness probably embarrass you and make you feel weak, vulnerable to injury and dependent upon the love and affection of others.

You are deeply hurt by rejection, especially after you gathered the courage to open yourself up. When this happens, you feel like withdrawing into your inner shell. You are sad and depressed. You want to give your love but your fear of being rejected makes it impossible. You feel you don't know how to love, thus reinforcing your shortcomings and inability.

You may compensate for your lack of love by adopting an extremely friendly personality, treating people equally in an impersonal manner without genuine involvement. When your heart is called for, you may evade the situation and shut yourself off because you are afraid of possible injury. If your Heart Chakra is completely closed, you will express coldness, indifference or even "heartlessness." You are completely out of balance and suffer from depression. Sadly, unhappiness is a way of life for you.

*One centerd in this chakra will be motivated by love. They will be concerned about balance and finding the natural rhythm of things.*

# Throat Chakra
## Claim Your Voice

## Purification

The Visudda or Throat Chakra is situated in the throat, at the base of the neck between the collar bone and shoulders, at the site of the reptilian brain or lower brain stem. Its name means pure.

It is associated, in the body with the throat, ears, thyroid, parathyroid, with the element ether, and the colour royal blue.

**Human Challenge and Gift**: To fearlessly express our truth and hear the sound of the universe.

**Soul Desire**: To be heard and understood, to transmit and receive the Truth.

**Primal Relationship**: With our vibrational connection with all existence.

**Fundamental Principle**: Resonance of being

**Body Association**: Neck, throat, jaw, ears, voice, trachea, bronchial tubes, upper lungs, esophagus and arms

**Gland**: Thyroid, which regulates the transformation of food into energy via our metabolism. It also controls the iodine metabolism and the balance of calcium in our blood and tissue.

Fig. 5.6: 5th Chakra - throat, blue, throat, ether, sound, communication, creativity, expansion, excitement, deer

| Throat Chakra | |
|---|---|
| **Colour Association** | Blue |
| **Sanskrit Name** | Visuddha |
| **Key notes** | Creative expression, communication |
| **Verb** | I communicate |
| **Force** | Vibration |
| **Location** | Throat region |

| Lesson | Relationships–The right to speak. Learning to express oneself and one's beliefs (truthful expression). Ability to trust. Loyalty. Organization and planning |
|---|---|
| Imbalances | Thyroid imbalances, swollen glands. Fevers and flu. Infections. Mouth, jaw, tongue, neck and shoulders problems. Hyperactivity. Hormonal disorders such as PMS, mood swings, bloating and menopause |
| Element | Ether |
| Celestial body | Mercury |
| Animal | Lion, deer, cat |
| Sense | Hearing |
| Food | Fruit |
| Throat Stimulants | Singing (in the shower), poetry, stamp or art collecting. Meaningful conversations. Blue food & drink. Blue gemstones and blue clothing. Using blue oils such as chamomile or geranium essential oils |

## Purpose and Function

The 5th chakra (Throat Chakra) is located between the depression in the neck and the larynx, beginning at the cervical vertebra. It starts at the cervical vertebra and opens towards the front. It is also connected to a small secondary chakra which has its seat in the neck (and opens to the back.) Since the two chakras are so closely related, they have been integrated as one.

The Throat Chakra is the center of the human capacity of expression, communication and inspiration and is connected to a smaller secondary chakra, which has its seat in the neck and opens to the back. Since they are so closely linked, they are integrated together as the Throat Chakra.

As an important link between the lower chakras and the Crown Chakra, the Throat Chakra serves as a bridge between our thoughts and feeling, impulses and reactions. Here we express our laughter, crying, feelings of love and happiness, anxiety, aggressiveness, intentions, desires, as well as our ideas, knowledge and perceptions of the inner worlds.

The Throat Chakra enables us to reflect on our thoughts and actions. The more we develop the Throat Chakra, the more aware we are of our mental body and our ability to distinguish between our mental and emotional, ethereal and physical bodies. As a result, our thoughts are no longer dominated by our feelings and physical sensations.

Ether is regarded in Yoga teaching as the basic element which forms the lower chakras -- earth, water, fire and air. The light blue colour of ether is the medium of the spoken word and the communicating element of information. If we are calm and listen to our inner and outer space, we will be granted the deepest level of knowledge, known as the Akasha (the astral light where all the events, thoughts and feelings that have occurred since the beginning of time are recorded.)

We communicate our inner life through the spoken word, as well as through gestures and creative forms of expression (i.e. music, the performing arts, dancing, etc.). The Sacral Chakra and the Throat Chakra link with the energies of the other chakras into an etheric form which is communicated to the outside worl. Since we can only express that which we find in ourselves, we need to distance ourselves in order to reflect on our thoughts and actions. The Throat Chakra enables us this certain distance. In other words, we need to develop the Throat Chakra in order to become more conscious of our mental body and distinguish between the factors of the mental, emotional, ethereal and physical bodies. In this way our thoughts are no longer dominated by feelings and physical sensations.

Hearing is also assigned to the Throat Chakra. Open your ears and listen to the voices of Creation. Here we also hear our inner voice and communicate with our inner spirit and receive inspiration.

## Harmonious Functioning

When the Throat Chakra is completely open, your feelings, thoughts and inner knowledge are expressed freely and without fear. You express your inner honesty towards yourself and others by your upright posture.

You possess the ability to fully express yourself with your entire personality, and at the same time, you remain silent and listen to others with all your heart and understanding. Your speech is imaginative and colourful and perfectly clear, and your voice is full and melodious. When faced with difficulties and resistance you are able to say "no", if that is what you truly mean. You are not swayed or manipulated by people's opinions. You maintain your independence, freedom and self-determination. You have no prejudices. You are open and aware of the reality of the subtle dimensions from which you receive the guidance of your inner voice. You trust yourself in the hands of this guidance. You possess the capability to communicate directly with life of all spheres of existence, and where applicable, you pass the knowledge you have gained onto others without fearing their reactions and opinions.

## Disharmonious Functioning

If the energies in your Throat Chakra are blocked or closed, then the communication link between your mind and body will be blocked - Either you find it difficult to reflect upon your feelings and you express your unresolved emotions in thoughtless actions, or, you may hide inside your intellect and deny your emotions a right to live and be heard. The only feelings you permit are those which you have self-judged and that do not contradict the judgement of the people around you. You have an unconscious feeling of guilt and your own inherent fears prevent you from seeing and showing your true Self. You cannot express your deepest thoughts and feelings freely.

Your language may be noisy, unpleasant and offensive, or cold, indifferent and business-like. You may stutter. Your voice is loud but your words lack depth of meaning. You try to appear strong; you do not permit yourself to show any weakness; and you probably place yourself under a lot of pressure.

You use your excessive expressive capabilities to manipulate others or to attract attention to yourself. Although you may possess deep, inner knowledge, you are afraid to live and/or express it because you fear judgement from others. In order to release this deep knowledge, you may express it in the form of poems, paintings or other forms of similar expression, then reluctantly, openly share it with others.

You cannot show and express yourself well, if at all. You withdraw your inner Self completely. You are shy, quiet, withdrawn, and when you talk, you talk about trivial matters.

You quickly get a lump in your throat if you try to express your deeper thoughts and feelings. Your voice sounds forced. When this happens, you may stutter. You feel uncertain. You are afraid of the judgement of others. You are out of touch with your soul, therefore, you do not trust your intuitive powers.

If you do not develop your Throat Chakra, you will find yourself imprisoned in a small restrictive space surrounded by your own self-built walls.

Your insecurities dominate your life.

*One centerd in this chakra will have an deep need to express themselves. They are very capable of resolving aspects of communication.*

# Third Eye Chakra
## Internal Reflection

## Perception

The *Ajana* or *Third Eye Chakra*, is located between the brows in the inward, center of the forehead. Its name means command, perception, knowledge, authority.

It is associated, in the body with the pituitary gland, eyes, brain, with the element light and also beyond the elements, and with the colours purple and indigo.

**Human Challenge and Gift**: To move from dualistic mind to intuitive neutral mind.

**Soul Desire**: To focus the mind, where one-pointed clarity and peace automatically occur.

**Primal Relationship**: With inner and cosmic knowledge.

**Fundamental Principle**: Knowledge of being.

**Body Association**: Face, eyes, ears, nose, sinuses, cerebellum, and central nervous system.

**Gland**: Pituitary. It is sometimes referred to as the "master gland." It is like the conductor of an orchestra, its secretional activities control the function of the other glands.

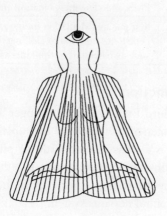

Fig. 5.7: 6th Chakra - (third eye or adjna center) forehead, indigo, forehead, light, clairvoyance, psychic abilities, imagination, dreaming, owl

| Brow or Third Eye Chakra | |
|---|---|
| **Colour Association** | Indigo, yellow, yellow-green or violet |
| **Sanskrit Name** | Anja |
| **Key notes** | Vision, perception, sixth sense |

| Verb | I see, I perceive |
|---|---|
| Force | Psychic |
| Location | Forehead, in between the eyes. |
| Lesson | Intuition–The right to "see." Trusting one's intuition and insights. Developing one's psychic abilities. Self-realization. Releasing hidden and repressed negative thoughts |
| Imbalances | Learning disabilities, co-ordination problems, sleep disorders |
| Element | Light |
| Celestial body | Jupiter |
| Animal | Owl, unicorn |
| Sense | Sight, sound, smell, taste and touch, also extrasensory perception |
| Food | Fasting, some cultures use hallucinogenic plants. |
| Depression | Thyroid imbalances, swollen glands. Fevers and flu. Infections. Mouth, jaw, tongue, neck and shoulders problems. Hyperactivity. Hormonal disorders such as PMS, mood swings, bloating and menopause |
| Brow Stimulants | Star gazing. Mediation Indigo food & drink. Indigo gemstones and indigo clothing. Using indigo oils such as patchouli or frankincense essential oils |

## Purpose and Function

The 6th chakra (Third Eye) is located a finger above the bridge of the nose in the center of the forehead and opens to the front. The Third Eye Chakra is also associated with the pituitary gland. Here, conscious perception of being takes place. It is the seat of our higher mental powers. On the physical plane, it is the highest center of command for the central nervous system.

Although indigo blue is normally associated with the Third Eye Chakra, yellow, yellow-green and violet can also be seen under meditation. These colours indicate different functions at different levels of consciousness. For example, rational or intellectual thought may produce yellow radiation; intuition and holistic cognition, a clear, dark-blue; and extrasensory perception, shades of violet.

Every realization in our lives begins with a thought and a projected image. By our mental powers, we are connected with the process of manifestation via the Third Eye. It is important to understand that all knowledge manifested in Creation already exists. This knowledge is all contained in the pure Being in the same way a seed contains all the information of the finished plant. In Quantum physics, this is also known as the "standardized field."

The shapelessness being manifests first a pattern of vibration. Then, from this first vibration, each step in the development of awareness creates a new and differentiated pattern of vibration. From the pure ethereal being to the denseness of matter, all levels of creation are contained in human life. These levels of creation are represented in the chakras with their various levels of vibration; thus, the process of manifestation takes place within and through us.

The Third Eye is the seat of consciousness attainment. Herein we can manifest matter and dematerialize it. We can create new realities and dissolve old ones. For the most part, this is an automatic process that takes place without any conscious action on our part. Most of our decisive thoughts are controlled by unresolved emotional patterns, which are programmed by our opinions and prejudices and those of others. As a result, our MIND is often NOT the Master but the Servant of our emotional thoughts.

By developing our consciousness and Third Eye Chakra, we can control our lives. Our imagination can create the energy necessary for the fulfilment of our wishes. And, when IN CONJUNCTION WITH an open Heart Chakra, we can send out healing energies to those close at hand and far away.

At the same time, we can gain access to all levels of creation beyond the physical reality. This knowledge manifests itself in the form of INTUITION, CLAIRVOYANCE, or the HYPERSENSITIVITY of hearing or feeling. Things that were vaguely suspected before are now perceived very clearly.

## Harmonious Functioning

Very few people today have a completely open Third Eye without an advanced state of consciousness. The Third Eye Chakra needs to be DEVELOPED! However, there are telltale signs of a harmonious functioning Third Eye, such as, an active mind and advanced intellectual skills (i.e. a compelling holistic pursuit of scientific research, or the recognition of far-reaching philosophical truths may be a sign of a partially open and harmoniously functioning Third Eye.)

You possess a well-developed ability of visualization and comprehension of things intuitively. You are receptive to mystic truths. You realize more and more that the world is but an allegory, a spiritual principle that has manifested itself on the physical level. From time to time, you notice that your thoughts or ideas have come true. If you develop your Third Eye completely, you will perceive the world in a new light. Your thinking will be holographic. You will perceive and spontaneously integrate the information from different spheres of creation into your growing capability of all-consciousness/awareness. The material world will become transparent to you. Your conscious is a mirror for the Divine, and the material world a mirror for the energy that exists on all levels of being.

Your extrasensory perception is so clear you directly perceive the energies at work beneath the surface of the physical world, and you realize that you can consciously control these energies AND create your own forms of manifestation.

Your intuition and inner sight will open the doors to all the subtle planes/dimensions of reality, which consist of an endless number of worlds between the physical (materialistic) planes of creation and pure Being. And you will realize that these other worlds/dimensions are inhabited by a wide variety of life forms.

## Disharmonious Functioning

You are what is considered, "top-heavy." You live completely in the realm of your mental sphere. Your life is determined almost exclusively by reason and intellect. All aspects of your life are organized in an intellectual manner; therefore, you can only perceive with your rational mind. Although your intellectual skills may be very sharp and well developed, and you may have a keen analytical ability, you lack a holistic way of seeing things.

You can easily fall prey to intellectual arrogance. You accept only those things that your mind can comprehend and that can be demonstrated and proven by scientific analysis. You perceive spiritual insight as unscientific and unrealistic and reject them outright.

You may attempt to influence others or events by intellectual force to demonstrate your power, satisfy your personal needs, and/or feed your ego. In this case, your Solar Plexus Chakra is usually out of balance and your Heart and Crown Chakra are only developed to a slight degree. All the Chakras play a part in the whole Being!

Your life is dominated by materialistic desires and physical needs without emotional consideration. You find spiritual reflection and discussion a strain and waste of time. You view spiritual truths as senseless dreaming without any practical use. Your thoughts are strictly aligned with the conventional lines of societal thought.

You easily lose your temper in demanding situations. You are also probably very forgetful. In extreme cases, your thinking will be muddled and confused and completely determined by unresolved emotional patterns. You are blind, deaf and dumb to the spiritual realms of sight, sound and speech. The only reality you see, hear, speak and accept is the physical, external, visible world.

In the grand scale of Life, your world is very small.

*One centerd in this chakra will see things a little different than most. They will find clarity wherever they focus with the use of inner sight.*

# Crown Chakra
## Merge

## Infinite

The Sahashrara or Crown Chakra, is located at the crown or top of the head, baby's soft spot. Its name means "thousand petal lotus".

It is associated, in the body with the pineal gland & cerebral cortex, with consciousness and beyond the elements, and with the colours white, silver and the quality of luminosity.

**Human Challenge and Gift**: To tune into and surrender to divine consciousness.

**Soul Desire**: To connect with and utilize infinite energies, to know the unknown, to experience the transcendental meaning to life.

**Primal Feeling**: Oneness, bliss.

**Fundamental Principle**: Purest being.

**Body Association**: Cerebrum.

**Gland**: Pineal.

Fig. 5.8: 7th Chakra - top of head, violet, top of head, thought, spiritual connection, understanding, knowing, bliss, God

| Crown Chakra | |
|---|---|
| Colour Association | Violet, also white |
| Sanskrit Name | Sahasrara |
| Key note | Divine knowledge, bliss |
| Verb | I accept, I |
| Force | Consciousness |
| Location | Top of head |
| Lesson | Knowingness–The right to aspire. Dedication to the divine consciousness and trusting the universe. Learning about one's spirituality. Our connection to the concept of "God" or a higher intelligence. Integrating one's consciousness and subconsciousness into the superconsciousness |
| Element | Thought |
| Celestial body | Uranus |
| Imbalances | Headaches. Photosensitivity. Mental illness. Neuralgia.Senility. Right/left brain disorders and coordination problems. Epilepsy. Varicose veins and blood vessel problems. Skin Rashes |
| Food | Fasting |
| Crown Stimulants | Focusing on dreams. Writing down one's visions and inventions. Violet food & drink. Violet gemstones and violet clothing. Using violet oils such as lavender or jasmine essential oils |

## Purpose and Function

The 7th chakra (Crown Chakra) is located at the middle of the head and opens upward. The Crown Chakra is also associated with the pineal gland, which is located in the middle of the head between the ears. The Crown Chakra is often represented in religious paintings as a halo above the head. Its predominant colour is violet, but it glows in all the colours of the rainbow.

The Crown Chakra unites in itself all the energies of the lower chakra centers. It is the source of energy for all the other chakras. Here we started our journey into life, and at the end of our development, this is where we will return. Here we live and experience UNITY with the primordial Divine principle and where our personal energy field becomes ONE with the universe.

The awareness the Crown Chakra gives us dwarfs the knowledge the Third Eye Chakra conveys. We now completely comprehend our intellectual and intuitive understanding. We experience our bodies as an expression of Creation as the divine consciousness of which we have become a part.

The colour violet is associated with the unfolding of the Crown Chakra. It is the colour of meditation and devotion. Albeit we can consciously influence the activation of all our lower chakras, with the Crown Chakra all we can do is open ourselves up to its influence and allow things to happen through us.

With the unfolding of the Crown Chakra, any blockages that may remain in the lower six chakras dissolve and their energies will begin to vibrate at their highest possible frequencies, each chakra working at its own level as a mirror of the Divine Being.

When the Crown Chakra is completely awakened, it ceases to absorb the cosmic energies and starts to radiate its own energy. A lotus blossom blossoms out, so to speak, and forms a crown of pure white light on and above the head. This same energy is portrayed in the artistic paintings of Jesus the Christ as a crown of white light radiating from the top of his head.

## Harmonious Functioning

The Crown Chakra can only be developed to a greater or lesser extent; your development with the other six chakras determines the degree. There are no blockages as such in the Crown Chakra. When the Crown Chakra begins to open, your consciousness will become completely calm and open. You will experience your real Self and realize that your Self is part of the omnipresent pure Being which is contained in all matter. As you develop your Crown Chakra, these moments will occur more frequently.

When your Self is ready for this final step of enlightenment, you will know. One day you will feel as if you have just awakened from a long dream of illusion, and for the first time you see the real reality of life. There is no turning back in your development now. You realize that what you have found is your true Self. Your individual ego has been transformed into a universal ego. If you want to know something, all you need to do is ask by directing your attention accordingly. Everything exists within you. You are ONE with the divine Being, and it is through this ONENESS that the ALL exists.

You now realize that matter is nothing but a form of thought in the Divine Consciousness and that it does not really "exists" as such. All that you thought was real up to this point you now perceive as an illusion.

Interestingly enough, you are open to the energies of the Crown Chakra every seven years. The seven year cycles are: ages 7, 14, 21, 28, 35, 42, 49, 56, 63, 70... During this period, you can develop a depth and insight and wholeness that you would have considered impossible before. Meditation and selfless devotion now provide you with insight into your Divine origin. This helps you experience a feeling of ONENESS. Use this opportunity to dwell more within yourself. Meditate. This is a seemingly magical time in your life.

It is also interesting to note that an infant's fontanel remains open for the first 9-24 months of its life, and it is during this particular period in their life when they live in an awareness (consciousness) of undivided unity.

## Closed Crown Chakra Characteristics

Up to this point, we have been told how the opening and harmonization of all the chakras can provide us with a great deal of knowledge, experience and skills. But if we do not open the Crown Chakra, we will feel separated from abundance and wholeness. We will not be completely free from fear, and it is this fear that always maintains some remnants of blockages within the chakras, therefore, they are unable to unfold our chakras complete range of possibilities. Their individual energies will not vibrate in complete harmony with the "dance of creation," nor with each other.

You may experience feelings of uncertainty and a lack of purpose if you do not open yourself to spiritual truths during the years when your Crown Chakra can develop. You should interpret these feelings as a hint to look inside yourself more frequently. Additionally, you may become more conscious of a certain senselessness in your life, or the fear of death may visit you more frequently. You may control these feelings by escaping into excessive activity, keeping yourself busy, or you may burden yourself with new responsibilities. Quite often, people in this condition fall ill. If you ignore these profound messages, your life may become a life stuck in superficiality. As a consequence, you limit the potential of your Self to develop. In essence, opportunity lost.

*One centerd in this chakra will have experienced a reality beyond the physical senses. One will be conscious of the infinite and know the unknown.*

## To summarize:

Fig. 5.9

*The Seventh Chakra or Crown chakra* is located at the top of the head. It externalizes as the pineal gland and governs the upper brain and right eye. Through this chakra one may ultimately reach the feeling of integration with God. Its colour is seen as violet or sometimes the combination of all colours: white light.

Fig. 5.10

*The Sixth Chakra or third eye is* located in the center of the forehead. It externalizes as the pituitary gland, governing the lower brain and nervous system, the ears, nose and the left eye, the eye of personality. Through this center we consider our spiritual nature. It is seen as the colour indigo - a vibrant combination of red and blue.

Fig. 5.11

*The Fifth Chakra* or *throat* area externalizes as the thyroid gland, and governs the lungs, vocal cords, bronchial apparatus, and metabolism. The center of expression, communication and judgment. It is seen as the colour blue.

Fig. 5.12

*The Fourth Chakra* is the *heart*, it externalizes as the thymus gland governing the heart, blood, and circulatory system and influences the immune and endocrine systems. This is the center through which we love. It is the colour green.

Fig. 5.13

*The Third Chakra* is located in the *solar plexus* externalizing as the pancreas, governs the action of the spleen, gall bladder, and aspects of the nervous system. It is the clearinghouse for emotional sensitivities and issues of personal power. It is the colour yellow.

Fig. 5.14

*The Second Chakra* is located in the *sexual organs* (ovaries in women and testes in men) and is the chakra of creativity. It governs attitudes in relationships, sex, and reproduction. It is the colour orange.

Fig. 5.15:
(Refer plate III for colour picture)

*The First Chakra*, the base or root is located at the *base of the spine* and is defined as that chakra that governs understanding of the physical dimension. It is the energy center through which one experiences fight or flight. Externalizing as the adrenal gland, governs the kidneys and the spinal column. It is perceived as the colour red.

## The Seven Major Chakras

| Chakra | Location | Colour | Sound | Domainand Characteristics |
|--------|----------|--------|-------|---------------------------|
| Crown Chakra, 7th, Sahasrara | Crown of Head | Violet | Aum | Governs brain, nerves, Soul energy. Forms spiritual awareness, Divine Energy |
| Third Eye, 6th, Ajna | Center of Forehead | Indigo | OM | Pituitary, pineal glands, Spinal cord, Eyes, ears, Sinuses. Spiritual Intuition. Knowledge of Higher Self |
| Throat Chakra, 5th, Vishuddha | Center of Throat | Sky Blue | HUM | Vocal cords, Thyroid, neck, mouth. Communication, Voice, Awareness of own needs, Is knowledge in motion |
| Heart Chakra, 4th, Anahata | Center of Chest | Green or Pink | YAM | Heart, lungs, diaphragm, breasts, Circulation, Breathe. Ability to give or receive. Unconditional love. Expression of Spiritual feelings |
| Solar Plexus, 3rd, Manipura | Diaphragm | Yellow | RAM | Liver, stomach, pancreas, kidneys, adrenals, Digestion. Seat of Will and Manifestation Amount of personal Power, Control |
| Creative or Sexual Chakra, 2nd, Swadhisthana | Lower Abdomen | Orange | VAM | Reproductive System, Bladder, Intestines. Level of Creativity, Sexual Expression, Energy of Self-Affirmation |
| Root Chakra, 1st, Muladhara | Perineum | Red | LAM | Coccyx, Sacrum, Rectum Level of Groundness, Survival Instinct. Link to the earth, Forms your perception of reality |

Briefly the root chakra is the physical center ( fulcrum, and support of the physical body) the root of beingness. The water chakra is the integrative creative, sensate, instinctual communication center. The fire chakra (navel) is the energetic/regenerative dynamo. The heart center (anahata chakra) is the integrative emotional and feeling center (this society teaches us to overcome, transcend, or ignore our feelings), the throat chakra (vishuddha) is the integrative cognitive communication center for the will and intellect (it integrates the head with the body in activity). The third eye (ajna chakra) is intuitive center of awareness and consciousness, while the crown chakra is the eternal spiritual center which partially lies outside of the body linking us with the ineffable, unbegun, never-ending, unformed, non-differentiated, formless, and timeless.

The upper chakras relate more to the more subtle forces of emotions, mental states, psychology, and belief systems while the lower centers are more primitive, vital, natural, and physical (furthermost removed from cognitive dominance). All of these relationships must be experienced as an interdependent ecology as a whole while memorization will be counterproductive. This is pointed out to suggest the possibilities to invite distinction, subtle differentiation, and perhaps diagnosis and treatment.

# Chapter 6

# Dis-Ease, A Curative Expression Of The Soul

Homeopathy is such a wonderful healing tool. It not only heals from the mental, emotional down to the physical level, but also has the power to take away the inherent miasms layer by layer. So, a deep pathological manifestation such as cancer, then, ought not to happen. But, well, it does happen.

Are diseases and addictions to be a part of life's reality just as aging and death? If we can change and grow in consciousness the answer will have to be no. Diseases and addictive behaviour can be considered as the physical and emotional expressions of an inner reality of the soul, or in Jungian terms, of the "psychological complexes." They are part of one-self and therefore are creative expressions of the soul when other avenues for expressing our creative energies (e.g. ability to speak one's truth) are blocked.

We are able to see how we express our own energies or inner reality when these are reflected outwardly as concrete events. Just as a mirror reflects whatever comes before it, so life's balance is constantly maintained in the dance of the inner and outer realities. The inner and outer (or the apparent opposing forces) are aspects of the same thing seen from different points of view. The more we identify with one end of polarity (e.g. light and dark) the more likely the opposite will come into manifestation as external events, because the opposite of the pole is yet to be consciously integrated into the personality. Physical diseases or life's happenings are reflections through which we might understand how we are managing our energies. If we are willing to look at the reflections, our awareness of such could lead to changes within ourselves; we may become less polarized and more balanced or aligned to our soul purpose. When disease/illness is considered as an expression of the soul we may realize that our individual self at its deepest level holds the key to healing.

# Chapter 7

# Homeopathy as a Vibrational Medicine

*"The material organism derives all sensibility and produces its life function solely by means of the immaterial wesen (the life principle, the life force) that enlivens the material organism in health and in disease"* (Organon, §10).

Healing in homeopathy is to take place at the level of the dynamic spirit-like life force with remedies that embody pure energy with *"no-thing"* in them.

If the remedies selected (simillimum) are to heal, they must also be resonant (more powerfully) with a similar vibrational frequency band in our individual life force, our mind and emotional energies. The challenge in practicing homeopathy, then, is to *find the core essence* of an individual (the foundation for the expression of one's life force) and its corresponding vibration found in a remedy. This explains why our primary concern in case taking should be to *elicit the mental and emotional patterns that reflect an individual essence*, with less emphasis on the physical disease symptoms.

Scholten's *Element Theory* and Sankaran's *Miasmatic Approach* provide us with a window into an individual's essence. The idea of the *"essences"* is not new. Homeopathy was taken a step further, in the seventies, when Vithoulkas explored the essence of the remedies.

If we look at the physical manifestation from the stance of individual essence, then, the disease symptoms are only secondary and consequential to the activities at the higher spiritual level. They are, therefore, particular, peculiar, incidental, or idiosyncratic to each individual in accordance with one's own constitutional make-up and state of consciousness. When the essence of an individual, the core of the problem, is understood and healed, the healing of physical symptoms will follow.

Yet, as a profession, we are still unable to step beyond the constraints of tradition to embrace the new tools that have every potential to increase our knowledge and hone our skill as healers. This said, there is still the inclination to give more weight and value to the proving symptoms over the clinical ones, which is a tradition that could become shackles around our feet. It begs the question: *"Are we in the profession of healing (clinical symptoms) or are we in the business of up-holding tradition in spite of the changing nature of diseases, environments, and consciousness?"*

The word *"proving"* means just that, to prove. Cured symptoms are clinical provings of what a remedy is capable of healing. The traditional full proving reveals those symptoms that a remedy could possibly heal, but not necessarily so. Inherent in the traditional proving symptom picture is the unavoidable bias resulting from the inability to take the provers individual idiosyncrasy out of the picture. If we take our bias in favouring the traditional full proving out of the equation of healing, what is left is a remedy that can heal if it is truly the simillimum to the individual. What it cures are the clinical symptoms.

The approach of Scholten and Sankaran addresses this level of healing, and also vastly expands the very concept of homeopathy as a vibrational medicine, because *the core essence of an individual is energy*. Their methodologies may appear to be deviant for many practitioners, but in fact they are extensions of the same tradition. We may consider their methods outlandish because they challenge us, as homeopaths, to truly know the essence of an individual. Although physical symptoms can point to a likely remedy, these are not the determining factor for prescribing a remedy (with the exception of a few first aid remedies). After all, homeopathy is a healing modality that works from the top down rather than from below upward.

All thoughts, emotions, spoken words, etc. create their own vibrational signature that profoundly affects one's cellular structure over time. If we trace the path of a disease manifestation, we may come to know what an individual needs to change to bring about the balance required for healing to take place. When homeopathic remedies heal at the vibrational level they can change the quality of the vital force.

## Vital Force

Homoeopathy considers the dis-ease condition to be the result of a weakened or disturbed vital force – "disease as a dynamic expression of the disturbance of the harmony and rhythm of the vital energy" (Roberts, 1982:37). There cannot be disease if vital force is in harmony and synchronized with life's creative expression. The centrality of vital force in health and disease is found throughout ancient civilizations, i.e. Chi in the Chinese traditional medicine. The Hindu concept of Prana expresses a similar idea.

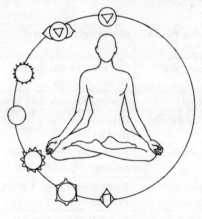

Fig. 7.1

In Chinese medicine, the concept of Chi relates to the life force that animates and energizes living organisms by way of the complex meridian system. The state of health, according to the Chinese, depends upon the balance of all the elemental forces of air, water, fire, earth, and metal. Prana commonly refers to the universal energy related to the breathe, but is in fact the basic constituent and source of all life.

In addition to the vital force having its conceptual equivalent to both Chi and Prana, vital force can also to be considered as another name for the human aura, which is an energy field with many layers surrounding the physical body. This energy field is intricately linked to our physical body via the seven major chakras – the energy vortices. These are vortices for energies to flow in and out of our auric field.

Each of the seven major chakras metabolizes and distributes the universal life force that flows downward from the crown of the head and upward from the base of the torso (coccyx). They distribute the subtle currents along the energetic threads called nadis to the nervous system, the endocrine system, then to the blood to nourish the body. The chakras affect the levels of our hormonal secretion, influence our emotional state and mental perception, our immune system and our metabolism. The more freely the energy flows, the healthier we are. Illnesses are caused by the imbalance or the blocking of energy distribution in the body.

| Chakras | Nerve Plexus | Physiological System | Endocrine System |
|---|---|---|---|
| Base | Coccygeal | Governs Skeletal System (spine), Kidneys | Adrenal glands |
| Sacral | Sacral | Governs Reproductive System | Gonads |
| Solar Plexus | Solar Plexus | Digestive System, Liver, Gall Bladder | Pancreas |
| Heart | Heart Plexus | Heart & Blood, Circulatory System | Thymus |
| Throat | Cervical Plexus | Respiratory, Lungs, Larynx, Pharynx | Thyroid |
| Third Eye | Hypothalamus, Pituitary | Lower Brain, Autonomic Nervous System | Pituitary |
| Crown | Cerebral Cortex, Pineal | Upper Brain, Central Nervous System | Pineal |

The seven major chakras not only have a close relationship with our physiological functions but also correlate with the development of consciousness. It is in this inter-connectedness that each level of manifestation serves as a mirror to the others. The chakras thus may be considered as the gateways or exchange stations between our physiological system, the universal energy, and the energies emanated through individual belief systems and perceptions that impact on our thoughts, attitudes, emotions, feelings, etc. In turn, they may also determine and influence how we manifest our creative energies in our lives' events and in the state of health. Although the chakras are not physical entities in and of themselves, they have a powerful effect on the physical body – the embodiment of the spiritual energy on the physical plane. Our health and vitality depend on the proper functioning of the chakra system.

Just as each of the chakras is associated with a specific part of our physiological system, so they also relate to psychological developmental patterns. How well a chakra may function in its capacity as the "gateway" depends very much on one's experiences during the developmental stages of life, as well as one's development in consciousness through meeting life's demands and the many challenges one faces.

The exploration of the chakras here is to elucidate a link between the physical manifestations, the psychological pattern, and the development of consciousness. Our understanding of this interconnectedness can assist us to manage our creative energy more effectively, which could lead to healing of the self.

Any form of injury to the chakras may lead to conditions such as ungrounded fear, mistrust, skewed perceptions and distorted belief systems about oneself and others. These influence how one interprets one's place in the world, in turn, affecting one's value-based choices in life to create individual reality.

The first three chakras form the lower trinity - the foundation of our growth that enables one to effectively utilize one's inherent gifts and abilities. This foundation determines how one develops the higher aspects of human evolution represented by the upper trinity - from the fifth chakra to the seventh. The fourth chakra, the heart, is the center of balance - performing the task of synthesizing our entire energy system through Self-love. An open heart chakra brings about greater balance within the individual and the ensoulment of body, mind, and spirit. Ensoulment is related to one's ability to harmonize the opposites (polarities) within. As one becomes more centered and less polarized, this opens one up to be compassionate in action, and develops one's capacity to love and receive love.

Within this framework of the chakras our vital force is in constant flux. It can either be strengthened or weakened with our individual input of energies. For instance, the seventh chakra relates to Self-knowledge (knowledge of divinity within). As we increase our knowledge of the Self so our belief system changes in regard to *"who we really are"* – are we the Self, the ego, or both? How we attribute meaning to the events that irrevocably change our lives will influence our perception. In turn, our perception affects how we experience life – the universe always reflects back to us what we believe ourselves to be. A lack of Self-knowledge is accompanied by a belief system (e.g. I am superior, inferior or no good) that creates blocks in the mental body, which in turn affects the emotions, and finally the physical body.

The wounding experience gives rise to an instinctual emotional reaction and/or mental perception of a given situation, as if from a *"template."* This so called template is formed since birth, from one's earliest experiences through to the formative years. It is within this framework that Sankaran's concept of *"disease as delusions"* or as "survival response" can be understood in context. *"... all symptoms of a disease represent the survival mechanism called for in the original situation"* (Sankaran, 1999:31).

Healing is, then, about changing the "template" within oneself, and is connected with our ability to step beyond the veil of delusions by changing our individual belief systems (the foundation of core beliefs – the first chakra). If we believe something we accept it without questioning, if we question the validity of what we believe, it offers the opportunity to extend our knowledge and understanding. In time, one becomes less reactive (emotionally charged action), less calculating, and more spontaneous (third chakra) in a given situation.

As the wounding experience gives rise to impaired chakra function (e.g. delusion), and at the same time, attracts certain experiences that reinforce one's delusions - which may wound further there comes about a perpetual self-fulfilling prophesy. Disease symptoms are intrinsically related to areas weakened due to arrested development from trauma or abuse. For instance, the fourth chakra's developmental tasks relate to our experience of love and unconditional acceptance of self and others, which leads to a sense of connectedness to all life. Yet the experience of shaming, rejection, and constant criticism from those who *"supposedly"* love us unconditionally (e.g. parents), gives rise to the potential manifestation of diseases of the heart, lungs, etc. On an emotional level, the wounding of the fourth chakra creates the feeling of deprivation, which may be reinforced by each encounter in life – perceiving every action and every word uttered by others as a form of rejection (delusion that one is inordinately unworthy of love).

Another way of understanding delusions is through the eighteen stages in Scholten's Element Theory (the periodic table) – these symbolize not only the developmental curve of an individual but also reveal our unformed ego state (first stage), our ego identification or where we possibly get *"stuck"* – the delusions. For example, stage two's central delusion is that one is inferior. Hence one of the basic themes is *"lack of confidence"* in people needing a remedy from the elements belong to stage two (e.g. Beryllium, Magnesium, Calcarea, etc.).

Conversely, stage ten (culmination or summit of one's achievements) relates to the delusion that one is superior. The central theme that relates to this delusion is arrogance and haughtiness which are supported by one's perception of external achievements and social status, measured against social values in terms of success or failure. Without saying that one should not strive to achieve the best one can, how do we define success or failure if it is not a subjective and value laden judgment.

Any form of ego identification with external social, cultural or political values is always delusional. Delusions are the deviation from our true Self. When one identifies, for example, with the power appropriated from positions such as manager, President, etc. one is at risk of losing one's identity or fading into insignificance (stage 15) as this power can be taken away either through retirement or redundancy. Ultimately, there is no such a thing as success or failure only evolution in consciousness that creates a sense of ONENESS of all life through our experiences.

Every cell and every molecule in our body is conscious – listening to one's continuous commands as beliefs, thoughts, emotions, feelings, and attitudes. As a result, they are constantly changing and modulating themselves to send out the exact energetic signals to attract the circumstances and experiences that reflect who we are in the form of self-fulfilling prophecy.

The concept of *"self-fulfilling prophecy"* related above could be considered to be what we know as *"maintaining cause"* in homeopathy on a deeper psychological level. Maintaining cause is that which continuously keeps one from getting well and healthy in spite of the quality of healing one receives. For example, a tree planted on a wind swept cliff has the chance next to nil to grow into its original design, its magnificent self unless the causal factor be removed. It is from the deep recesses of one's *"maintaining cause"* that a well selected homeopathic remedy may only be effective for a short duration and lack the power to create more of a lasting effect so alters one's cellular expression. The more permanent changes may need to take place at the higher level by an individual's own resolve to heal the self.

In view from the above stated, the disease of cancer is not only deeply pathological, but is also embedded in deep hurt, and an unconscious sense of self-hatred and self-betrayal – an inability to truly express oneself creatively for fear of others' poisonous criticism, rejection, envy, etc. This line of reasoning does provide certain insight into the development of cancer in many cases, and explains the prominence of Cadmium combinations used in cancer treatment in homeopathy (especially in advanced cases – refers to Arthur Grimmer's Work).

Cadmium belongs to the Silver series, stage twelve in the Element Theory. According to Scholten, the main theme in the Silver series is the creative expression through arts, science, language, etc. Some characteristics associated to the stage twelve are as follows:

*"These people also like to maintain what they have achieved, but they go too far in trying to hold onto it. They have all sorts of plans to keep things as they are and there is no stopping them. They are very conservative in their outlook and as long as everything is going according to the old plans and routines they feel fine. They will immediately vote against change of any form or description. They don't really listen to others, and if they do it is only to pick up ideas that they can later use in their own schemes"*

The qualities elicited from the above quote can be summed up as being *"stubborn; holding on at all cost; unchanging."* It would be hard for one to truly create changes in one's negative perception about oneself with these qualities as part of the personality make-up. No homeopathic remedy or amount of radiation treatment can heal the deep delusional state that manifests as cancer. Only the soul's desire to be healed can affect a change and healing.

## Susceptibility

We can hardly discount the myriad causal factors, such as environmental toxins or emotional shock, to have an impact on our vitality. These often serve as a trigger for our innate susceptibility to the manifestation of diseases.

Susceptibility, from the traditional homeopathic perspective, can be defined as the reaction of the organism to external (e.g. environmental) and internal (e.g. emotional and mental) influences or stresses. Some of us are naturally more susceptible to addictions or diseases than others. Yet, monitoring susceptibility is another way of perceiving a weakened vital force.

Susceptibility may be related to our individual inherited emotional and psychological patterns. These reflect our wounded self and the effect of such is the alienation from our spiritual-core-self that leads to delusions. Ultimately, these patterns impact on our genetic make-up or may trigger our inherited genetic predisposition into manifesting addictions and certain bodily diseases. It follows, prior to the healing of one's addictive behaviour or physical diseases corresponding to the specific chakra/s can take place, the wounded psychological developmental issues will need to be addressed and healed first.

*Typically,* one's repeated reactivity (*"one's buttons being pushed"*) to a particular situation, person, or issue, reveals a wound that is yet to be healed. Our emotionally charged reaction is a sure sign that the original unconscious wounding (template) is being reactivated. The continued negative reaction (e.g. uncontrollable anger, fear of rejection) to the same stimuli can eventually weaken our vitality that leads to disease. One's wound is where lies one's *"susceptibility"* or predisposition to the development of certain diseases.

An individual can either become more susceptible by ways of continuous suppression or may lessen the innate susceptibility by having homoeopathic constitutional treatment or other forms of vibrational medicine. Susceptibility, like vital force, is a fluid, changeable condition. Homeopathic remedy reduces susceptibility and removes the predisposition to certain disease manifestations simply because the vibrational frequency of a remedy satisfies or neutralizes the frequency of the susceptibility that produced the sickness in the first place.

On an emotional and mental level, our innate susceptibility has a tendency to continue to recreate and attract to ourselves situations that meet our biochemical needs. This provides the same *"rush"* of emotions as the original wounding and reinforces what one comes to know as *"safe and familiar"*. These situations have a particular affinity for triggering certain disease conditions because they act like a key that unlocks the weakened physical area corresponding to the wounded chakra. This reveals the underlying causal factor as to why members of the same family have the tendency to exhibit the same emotional expressions (e.g. quick to anger in one parent and perhaps extreme passivity in another) or develop similar diseases (inherited genetic susceptibility). Extreme anger and undue passivity are two sides of the same coin (e.g. Magnesium). When the childhood developmental wounds begin to heal via a given remedy, one is likely to become more balanced - the *"Magnesium state"* is satisfied. (Refer to Scholten's *"Diagnosis Yellow-flower"* Interhomeopathy, July 2006).

Today's propensity toward taking a myriad drugs (for recreational or medical purposes), excessive alcohol consumption, ingesting food far beyond satiety, unbridled indulgence in sexual gratification, or gross display of emotions such as rage, murderess intent, etc. can be considered as a form of *"self-medication"* to give *"a quick fix"* to our inherent susceptibility. Addiction is not just about cravings for drugs but relates to one's inability to manage one's emotional or physical cravings. These are repeated acts of self-affirmation and self-medication.

A similar remedy satisfies a person's innate susceptibility (reducing the need to *"self-medicate"* with addictions), and the potency of a remedy affects the frequency levels of an individual. Brennan, a healer with the ability to perceive auras, observed in her work that: *"the higher the potency of the homeopathic remedy, the higher the auric body it affects. The higher potencies above 1M work on the higher four layers of the auric field and the lower potencies work on the lower auric levels"*. As our auric fields become more balanced by having homeopathic remedies, our vital force strengthens. Hence, the natural progression is a healthier body.

Addictions and diseases when understood the cause of their manifestations could be pathways to change and growth in consciousness.

# Disease as Pathway to the Self

Diseases and addictions are not incidental manifestations that come out of no where. Edgar Cayce explained it this way: *"All illness is sin. ... This doesn't means sins committed in the present life but sin expressing itself as illness, because it has not yet been expiated by the soul."* The word *"sin"* in this context, simply means the transgression of spiritual laws against oneself or another (e.g. self-loathing; hatred of another). It has nothing to do with morality or religiosity.

Another way of considering the purpose of illness is thus: *"Illness is a built-in service, a feeling based feedback system activated by harmful input stemming from a personal misuse of energy"* (Marciniack). Self-healing, therefore, is a journey not only involves in one learning to manage one's energy creatively, but is always accompanied by great personal courage and compassion for the self.

We need courage because to heal ourselves at the soul level involves fundamental changes in our belief system, in our emotional attachment to certain behaviour patterns, events and people, and in our perception. Healing could literally mean breaking off many familiar ties, which means letting go of self-negating psychological agreements with family members, friends, peers, and/or social values.

Those agreements of self-perception, habitual self-recrimination and self-condemnation through self-talk also need to be broken if one is to heal. One's perception of being superior or inferior to others is delusional (e.g. others are more beautiful physically, apparently more intelligent, have a bigger house, etc. than oneself). What is one's true state of being? All things external to oneself can be swept away by time and circumstances (unforeseen illnesses, catastrophe, etc.). What is left is pure consciousness.

In this healing process, one takes the risk of speaking one's own truth, perceiving oneself in a new light - which may be quite the opposite to how our parents, spouse, relatives, or friends perceive us or expect of us. This can be daunting because we are stepping out onto uncharted territories. It is much easier to walk the same old path, live the same old safe life, and allow the same old reactional behaviour to the same old stimuli, because these are effortless, comfortable, familiar, and instinctual (the limbic system in the brain). The old ways do not require us to make decisions or choices about *"who we really are"* or expend the effort to find out about what our values are - where our passion is. Courage also means truly believing in one's own worth so that the journey of self-healing is worth all the pain, trouble and effort, however difficult, challenging, or alone it may be. Essentially, one's own healing journey is that of a *"Hero's Quest"* (finding one's true self through confronting the challenges presented by life). On this quest, the moment one gains insight into the possibilities, there is carried the vibrational frequency which enlivens one's whole being. Then one is inexorably changed.

Compassion is a companion along the way we cannot afford to be without if we are to heal ourselves. The word compassion means *"suffering with"*. In the context of this essay, compassion is toward oneself – it means that one must be able to bear the pain of being a witness to one's own suffering. Self-healing is a journey on which we continuously define *"who we really are"* at the juncture of each conscious choice. It is akin to a journey into the underworld (the unconscious) to retrieve those precious bits and pieces discarded when growing up because one's parents or peers may have *"disapproved"*. For example, adults often teach children to tell *"a little white lie"* in order to hide family secrets from others. A little white lie (as opposed to the morally unacceptable lies), therefore, carries social and cultural agreements that allow one conveniently to get out of *"sticky"* situations without having to honour oneself and others, or going through the trouble of finding out one's own truth (the corresponding energetic center is the throat chakra) in relationship to the event. In time, this energetic blockage steps down to the physical manifestation of disease in areas related to this center.

The challenge for one not telling *"a little white lie"* is how we can be authentic in our encounters in life. The very essence of being authentic precludes any possibilities in causing others pain or harm and, at the same time, rules out habitual negative self-criticism, self-recrimination, or self-blame. One's decision to whether tell a little white lie or not, in a given situation, is not about the morally right or wrong thing to do, but has everything to do with how one manages one's energy because the energetic imprint behind such seemingly inconsequential *"little white lie"* is the alienation from the Self.

Honesty creates connections between individuals, whereas dishonesty generates an ever widening gap because our auric field is a broadcast station open to anyone who can read energies. As we acknowledge our own worth, rather than allowing ourselves to be manipulated or defined by social values and trends, or others' opinions, we come closer to the center of our own being that will lead to a more balanced self at every level. Cayce states *"healing of the physical without the change in the mental and spiritual aspects brings little real help to the individual in the end"*.

At the fundamental level, cancer can be considered as a symbolic representation of the state of our being - one literally consumes oneself from inside when the creative outer expression of the self is non-existent. If we cannot live a life that affirms *"Who We Really Are"* at every turn, then there is no deeper betrayal of the Self. Abandoning oneself in courting the collective values defined by external images and social masks generates an increasing sense of emptiness within. A life that affirms our true Self requires us living according to one's inner truths and obeys one's inner laws. This can only come about from one truly loving the Self/self (the heart chakra) in our encounters in life. *"Do we have a choice in every circumstance?"* Of course, we do. The question is whether or not we are prepared to pay the price that comes with every choice we make.

# Chapter 8

# Miasms

## Introduction

During the 18th century, the word 'miasm' was loosely used to denote the discharge coming from decaying animal or vegetable matter. It was also sometimes used to denote the discharge coming from bodies of diseased person. The morbific agents, which were thought to be connected with production of disease, were designated by a general term 'miasm'.

The use of this term by Hahnemann remains controversial. At some places in his writing, Hahnemann has used miasm to denote the predisposition for disease and at other places he has used it to denote the morbific agent, similar to bacteria & viruses, and the states arising from their suppression.

## History of Miasms

In the early days of his practice when Hahnemann started using the law of similars, he got good success in acute and epidemic diseases but he failed miserably in a large number of chronic diseases. He himself said – *"Their beginning was promising, the continuation less favourable, the outcome hopeless…"*

For example, if a patient came to him with pain in knee worse by initial motion and better by continued motion, he would have probably prescribed Rhus tox. If the cause of this symptom were acute, the patient would get cured. If the case were chronic (say arthritis or gout), the patient would often come back with the same symptoms after an initial amelioration.

Such instances made Dr. Hahnemann probe deeply into the concept of disease and the development of the chronic diseases. After 12 years of detailed case takings and case analysis, he found out that nearly all the patients with chronic diseases had a history of either Scabies, Syphilis, or Gonorrhoea and most of the patients were not well since the time of infection. He called these infections and the disease tendency arising from them, miasms. The one arising from Scabies was called Psora or non-venereal miasm. The other two were called venereal miasms as they arose from sexual conduct. The one arising from Syphilis was called Syphilitic miasma and the one from Gonorrhoea was called Sycotic miasm.

## The Divide

During the days of Hahnemann, homeopathic world was divided in two parts:

a.   Those who believed in miasms.

b.   Those who did not.

In the early days of this theory, very few of Hahnemann's pupils accepted this theory whole-heartedly. There were others like Hering who became converts with experience. There were still others like Richard Hughes who never believed it and even went on to call this theory of miasms, Hahnemann's biggest mistake.

Later with the rise of Kent and advent of microbiology/ bacteriology, even the believers split into two groups:

a.   Those who believed Hahnemann's miasm were nothing but bacteria and viruses.

b.   Those who believed in the spiritual nature of the miasms.

Dr. Hering, R. Hughes, Stuart Close, G. Boericke, Margret Tyler, P. Speight, B. K Sarkar, Harimohan Chaudhary – all have favoured the concept that miasms are bacteria or originate from bacterial diseases. Some of these people even went on to call Hahnemann as the Father of Bacteriology because his description of miasms was so similar to the bacteria at many places. Others like Kent, J. H. Allen, J. Paterson, H. A. Roberts etc. strongly believed in the non-material nature of the miasms. They described miasms as a dyscrasia, a state, and a predisposition. Kent even went on to say: "Psora is the underlying cause, the primitive or primary disorder of the human race…. it goes to the very primitive wrong of the human race, the very first sickness of the human race, that is the spiritual sickness.."

So the big question is what exactly Hahnemann meant when he used the term miasm? What was his concept of origin of chronic diseases?

If you go through various works of Hahnemann closely, you will realize that Hahnemann has used the term 'miasm' in the both senses at different places. May be he was himself a bit confused. On one hand he was talking about the spiritual vital force and its dynamic derangement as the cause of all disease, on the other hand he was well aware that there was something material (contagion) in acute diseases like Cholera and Typhus, and Chronic diseases like Syphilis and Gonorrhoea. We need to understand that Hahnemann was trying to understand the cause of disease without the aid of any microscopes. He was just relying on his keen observation and apart from his observation, there was nothing much to support him. Developing a whole classification of diseases was a marvellous work done by Hahnemann. He had his own limitations and the work he has done within those limitations is extraordinary.

In the following paragraphs from Chronic Diseases, Hahnemann shows to believe in the infectious nature of disease and considered miasms as infectious agents.

"The infection with miasmas, as well of the acute as of the above-mentioned chronic diseases, takes place, without doubt, in one single moment, and that moment, the one most favourable for infection.

What has nature been doing with the infection received in these ten or twelve days? Was it not necessary to first embody the disease in the whole organism before nature was enabled to kindle the fever, and to bring out the emption on the skin?

"In that part of the sexual organs where the infection has taken place, nothing unnatural is noticed in the first days, nothing diseased, inflamed or corroded; so also all washing and cleansing of the parts immediately after the impure coition is in vain. The spot remains healthy according to appearance, only the internal organism is called into activity by the infection (which occurs usually in a moment), so as to incorporate the venereal miasma and to become thoroughly diseased with the venereal malady.

On the other hand, are not the chronic miasmas disease-parasites which continue to live as long as the man seized by them is alive, and which have their fruit in the eruption originally produced by them (the itch-pustule, the chancre and the fig-wart, which in turn are capable of infecting others and which do not die off of themselves like the acute miasmas, but can only be exterminated and annihilated by a counter-infection, by means of the potency of a medicinal disease quite similar to it and stronger than it (the anti-psoric), so that the patient is delivered from them and recovers his health?)" (P35).

Also, in his article on Asiatic Cholera, published in 1831, Dr. Hahnemann has written:

"In those confined spaces, filled with mouldy water vapours, the cholera miasm finds a favourable element for its multiplication, and grows into an enormously increased brood of those excessively minute, invisible, living creatures, so inimical to human life, of which the contagious matter of cholera most probably consists".

In those paragraphs from Organon & Chronic Diseases, Hahnemann considered disease as dynamic, non-physical and the origin of chronic diseases as dynamic predisposition to disease.

"All miasmatic maladies which show peculiar local ailments on the skin are always present as internal maladies in the system

before they show their local symptoms, externally upon the skin.."
(32, CD).

"Is not, then, that which is cognizable by the senses in diseases
through the phenomena it displays, the disease itself in the eyes of the
physician, since he never can see the spiritual being that produces the
disease, the vital force?" (§6).

"He calls such effects dynamic, virtual, that is, such as result
from absolute, specific, pure energy and action of he one substance
upon the other substance.

For instance, the dynamic effect of the sick-making influences
upon healthy man, as well as the dynamic energy of the medicines
upon the principle of life in the restoration of health is nothing
else than infection and so not in any way material, not in any way
mechanical. Just as the energy of a magnet attracting a piece of iron
or steel is not material, not mechanical. A purely specific conceptual
influence communicated to the near child small-pox or measles in
the same way as the magnet communicated to the near needle the
magnetic property" (Footnote to §11).

"It is the morbidly affected vital energy alone that produces
disease, so that the morbid phenomena perceptible to our senses
express at the same time all the internal change, that is to say, the
whole morbid derangement of the internal dynamis; in a word, they
reveal the whole disease" (§12).

"Therefore disease (that does not come within the province of
manual surgery) considered, as it is by the allopathists, as a thing
separate from the living whole, from the organism and its animating
vital force, and hidden in the interior, be it ever so subtle a character,
is an absurdity" (§13).

"But as nothing is to be observed in diseases that must be
removed in order to change them into health besides the totality of
their signs and symptoms, and likewise medicines can show nothing
curative besides their tendency to produce morbid symptoms in
healthy persons and to remove them in diseased persons" (§22).

So we see that the confusion about the cause or origin of diseases was evident to a great extent in Hahnemann's writings even up to the 6th edition of the Organon. On one hand he was saying that nothing material could be found in sick persons as disease results from the dynamic derangement of the Vital Force and on the other hand he was describing microscopic living organisms as the cause of Cholera!

## Miasms in The Modern World

After Hahnemann, many homeopaths have suggested that since miasms are disease syndromes, there can be more miasms that psora, syphilis and sycosis. The concept is to look for diseases which leave a diseased state in the body even after apparent recovery, especially after suppression. In this regard, the following miasms have been proposed so far:

1.  Tubercular – J. H. Allen.
2.  Vaccinosis – Dr. Burnett.
3.  Cancer.
4.  Malaria – R. Sankaran.
5.  Ringworm – R. Sankaran.
6.  Typhoid – R. Sankaran.
7.  Leprosy – R. Sankaran.
8.  Smallpox.

The understanding and approach of those who have put forward newer miasms is varied and at odds with Hahnemann's ideas as well. Such differences arise from a different understanding and approach to the disease process. As a result of this the world of miasms has become more chaotic.

Now I will pick up 3 modern authors – Vithoulkas, Sankaran, and Vijayakar and probe into their approach and understanding of chronic miasms.

## George Vithoulkas

George Vithoulkas does not fall into the trap of whether miasms are bacteria or simple predisposition to disease. According to him it can be both – a predisposition acquired through a suppressed disease or other strong influences on the vital force like vaccination, strong emotional or mental shocks or a predisposition which is inherited from parents.

Vithoulkas defines miasms as:

"A miasm is a predisposition towards chronic disease underlying the acute manifestation of an illness:

1.  Which is transmissible from generation to generation.
2.  Which may respond beneficially to the corresponding nosode prepared from either pathological tissue or from the appropriate drug or vaccine."

He also says: "...any homeopath who has studied the course of degeneration of patients over a long period of time can attest to the presence of a large number of 'miasms'."

Vithoulkas believes that miasms appear as layers (of suppression?) in chronic cases, which need to be peeled one by one through medicines based on the totality of symptoms. Also Vithoulkas believes that any miasm can produce any pathology and the notion that tumours are sycotic, ulcers are syphilitic etc is wrong. Except for the fact that Vithoulkas considers there are many miasms, his approach to the miasms is very classical.

## Rajan Sankaran

In his work 'The Spirit of Homeopathy', Sankaran had described disease as 'delusion', the 'awareness' of which becomes a 'cure'. In his subsequent work 'The Substance of Homeopathy', he extends his approach to disease to the concept of miasms. Unlike others who developed their understanding of miasms through the cause and classification of diseases, Sankaran evolved his ideas of miasms by trying to find the common theme in the mental states and delusion of known anti-miasmatic remedies. From there he extended the concept to the physical and pathological states corresponding to the miasms.

For example, to develop an understanding of Psora he studied known anti-psoric remedies like Sulphur and Psorinum and compared their underlying theme, delusions and state to find the common miasmatic ground.

Sankaran says – "The acute (miasm) is the immediate reaction necessary to survive. Psora is the reaction to a situation which demands struggle with the circumstances outside in order to survive. Sycosis is the reaction to a situation that demands that he accepts his own weakness and cover it up to survive. The syphilitic reaction comes with the realization that adjustment is no longer sufficient and that in order to survive he must bring about a radical change in the internal or external circumstances, or both."

Sankaran's approach on the mental plane may seem radical to many but on the ground his use of physical symptoms of the miasms is very classical. The only difference is that Sankaran has come to hold the ear from behind the head! Sankaran has evolved his understanding of miasms with his understanding of medicines and their mental states.

The significant aspect of Sankaran's concept of miasms is his focus on newer miasms like Tubercular, Leprous, Cancer, Malarial, Typhoid and Ringworm. He says Typhoid miasm is a subacute miasm, which lies between the acute, and Psoric miasms. It has the main feeling of a critical situation, which, if properly handled for a critical period, will end in a total recovery. Ringworm miasm lies between Psora and Sycosis. It is characterized by an alteration between periods of struggle with anxiety about its success, and periods of despair and giving up. Malarial miasm, which lies between acute miasm and Sycosis, has an acute feeling of threat that comes up intermittently. Tubercular, Leprosy and Cancer miasm lie between Sycosis and Syphilis. In Tubercular miasm the feeling is of intense oppression and exploitation, and a desire for change. Cancer miasm has a feeling of weakness and incapacity within, with a desire for perfection. Leprosy has the feeling of intense oppression, intense hopelessness, and an intense desire for change.

The other difference in Sankaran's approach is his list of anti-miastmatic remedies. Since he uses a different classification of miasms and also relies on the 'state' of the patient to judge the miasm, he has his own list of antimiastmatic remedies.

I cannot dwell deeper on Sankaran's approach here but I would like to say that although Sankaran's miasms appear very different from Hahnemann's miasms, they are actually not. Sankaran has picked all his miasms from infections and uses physical symptoms too, to identify a miasm just like others. The difference in his work is that he has been able to associate different mental states with each miasm and the transition from one miasm to another is shown through successive changes in the mental state. The only drawback in Sankaran's approach is that his process relies so heavily on a specific method of case taking, analysis and understanding of mental states that it introduces a lot of subjectivity and others may find it difficult to get the same results by following his approach.

## Prafull Vijayakar

Vijayakar's approach to miasms is not new. He is using very classical Hahnmannian approach of Psora, Syphilis and Sycosis. The uniqueness in his approach lies in his understanding of these miasms.

Vijayakar's basic approach is similar to the established understanding of miasms: Psora is related to irritability, Sycosis to excess or deficient growth and Syphilis to destruction. But he does not seem to believe in the concept of infections as the primary source of the miasms. He correlates miasms with the cellular defense mechanisms. Dr. Vijayakar's approach is that mere symptom-similarity will not give results in chronic diseases, unless the underlying miasm of the patient is taken into consideration.

Vijaykar correlates the physiological defense of the cell with Psora, the constructive defense with Sycosis and the destructive defense with Syphilis. He says that everyone has all the three miasms but the type of cell-defense dominant in a person reflects his dominant miasm. Although novel, this approach to the understanding of miasms appears very one-sided and deficient in many aspects. The excessive focus on the cell to the exclusion of the 'whole' leaves lots of open-ended questions. He has tried to present miasms in a scientific garb but has not succeeded much in his efforts at a deeper level.

What he has succeeded in is clinical use of the miasms. If you leave his efforts to explain the miasms through genes and all, the rest of his clinical approach is very easy to follow and good indeed. Vijayakar's approach is to rely on the totality of the case, which includes the underlying miasm. Unlike Sankaran, who relies on current mental state of the patient, Vijayakar relies on the inherent mental traits (like conscientious, diligent etc) of the person to narrow down his search for the similimum. The way Vijaykar differentiates between the importance of medicines in a given case based on the underlying miasm is worth taking note of. The clinical approach of Vijaykar is very easy to follow and unlike Sankaran, has much less subjectivity.

After going through Hahnemann's works and understanding the way in which his thoughts evolved, it's easy to realize that the theory of miasms has three different aspects:

A.  Genetic or Inherent predisposition to acquire a disease.

B.  Acquired predisposition for chronic diseases – through suppression or use of allopathic / antipathic measures.

C.  Diseases which when untreated or maltreated, lead to chronic disease syndromes related to natural progression of disease or lead to an increase in susceptibility for other diseases.

Hahnemann has talked about all these aspects at one place or other but due to the lack of scientific advancements, he was not able to systematize his understanding of the cause of chronic diseases and chronic miasms. The confusion that is apparent in his works has trickled down to the homeopathic community since the time of Hahnemann. The reason for this is that while homeopaths are often dogmatic about what Hahnemann has written, they rarely try to understand why he wrote, what he wrote. The approach used by Kent, Vithoulkas, Sankaran and Vijayakar is just one-sided approach to this multi-dimensional theory. We need more work to systematize this concept and bring it upon a scientific platform.

## Physical expressions of the miasms

The mind and body work together as a unit and the disturbances are expressed in both spheres.

A. *Psoric Miasm:* Reaction of body on exposure to environmental stimuli to ones surroundings like noise, light, and odors, producing functional disturbances like headache, nausea, and discomfort.

B. *Sycotic Miasm:* Hypersensitive response to something specific arising from a deficiency of the normal response like tumours, allergies, keloids. Deficient feeling gives rise to an increased attempt to repair the fault.

C. *Syphlitic Miasm:* Not manageable, finding destruction like gangrene, ulceration. Body and mind destroy itself, give-up.

D. *Tubercular Miasm:* Respiratory imbalance, weak lungs, offensive, head-sweat, worse with exposure to cold, re-occurring epistaxis, bleeding gums, long eyelashes, craving for salt, enuresis, bleeding stools, milk disagrees causing diarrhoea, anaemic, weakness, ringworm, acne, white spots on nails, nightmares.

## Personality types

A. *Psoric Miasm:* Highs and lows, struggling with outside world, becomes apparent at times of stress, lack of confidence, constant anxiety feelings, fear, like he can't do it, insecurity, anxiety about the future but always having hope, mentally alert.

B. **Sycotic Miasms:** Secretiveness, hide his weakness, tense, constantly covering up situations, fixed habits, suspicious, jealous, forgetful.

C. **Syphlitic Miasm:** Strong pessimistic view on life, cannot modify what is wrong, give-up, destroy, no point in trying to adjust, sudden impulsive violence directed at himself or others, dictational rigid ideas. Mental paralysis, mentally dull, suicidal, stupid, stubborn, and homicidal.

D. **Tuburcular Miasm:** Dissatisfaction, lack of tolerance, changes everything, does harmful thing to one's self.

## General Nature of the Miasm

A. **Psoric Miasm:** Itching, burning, inflammation leading to congestion.- philosopher, selfish, restless, weak, fears.

B. **Sycotic Miasm:** Over production of growth like warts, condylomata, fibrous tissue, attack internal organs, pelvis, sexual organs.

C. **Syphlitic Miasm:** Destructive, disorder everywhere, ulceration, fissures, deformities, ignorance, suicidal, depressed, memory diminished.

D. **Tuburcular Miasm:** Changing symptomatology, vague, weakness, shifting in location, depletion, dissatisfaction, lack of tolerance, careless "problem child", cravings that are not good for them.

## Dermatological Symptoms of the Miasms

A. **Psoric Miasm:** Dirty, dry, itching without pus or discharge, burning, scaly eruptions, eczema, cracks in hands and feet, sweat profuse < during sleep offensive.

B. **Sycotic Miasm:** Warty, moles, unnatural thickening skin, herpes, scars, nails are thick and irregular---corrugated, oily skin with oozing, disturbed pigment in patches.

C. *Syphlitic Miasm:* Ulcers, boils, discharge of fluids and pus offensive, slow to heal, leprosy, copper coloured eruptions < by heat of bed, spoon shape thin nails that tear easily, gangrene putrid.

D. *Tuburcular Miasm:* Ringworm, eczema, urticaria, herpes, recurrent boils with pus and fever. Does not heal fast. Leprosy < by warmth of bed > by cold nails white spots.

# Pains of Miasms

A. *Psoric Miasm:* Neurological type, sore, bruised, >rest <motion.

B. *Sycotic Miasm:* Joint pains, rheumatic pains are < cold, damp > motion, stitching, pulsating, wandering.

C. *Syphlitic Miasm:* Bone Pains, tearing, bursting, burning.

D. *Tubercular Miasm:* Great exhaustion, never enough rest, sun> give strength.

# Miasms: Clinicals

A. *Psoric Miasm:* Acidity, burning, cancer, sarcomas, constipation, epilepsy, flatulence, hoarseness, itching of skin, leprosy, burning of spinal cord, watery discharge from nose and eyes with burning.

B. *Sycotic Miasm:* Abortion, acne without pus, angina pectoris, anaemia, appendicitis, cough (whooping), colic, pelvic disease + sexual organs, piles, prostatitis, nephritis (kidney), gout, arthritis, dry asthma, dysmenorrhoea, herpes, rheumatism, warts, urinary ailments.

C. *Syphlitic Miasm:* Discharges putrefaction, blindness, boil in veins and bones, carcinomas, fistula, fungal infection of extremities, gangrene, hyperextension, bone marrow inflammation, insanity due to depression, leucorrhoea, rheumatism of long bones, skin disease with ooze + pus, sore throat, history of abortions, sterility, immature death, cardiac attacks, suicidal deaths, insanity, cancer, tuberculosis, ulcers of ear, nose, urinary organs, mouth.

D. *Tubercular Miasm:* Aching pain in knees, swelling without any cause, asthma, bedwetting, cancer, carious teeth, destruction of bone marrow, diabetes, dry cough (barking), eczema, emaciation, epilepsy, extreme fatigue, weakness, glands enlarged, tonsils, influenza, insanity, obstruction of intestines, malaria, insomnia, nocturnal perspiration, palpitation, profuse haemorrhage of any orifice, pneumonia, ring worm, short temper, nasal coryza, worms.

The inheritance of the miasms is not genetic and actually takes place because the "vital force" of parents is tainted by such states. As observed with mother and father at time of conception. Miasms are seen to be transmitted to the offspring. It is not the pathology which shows the miasm but the state. The characteristics in that individual, keeping with the mental and physical state. The three together reflect the miasm. The mental = delusion and the physical = type of reaction. A disease state is usually a combination of miasms with it's main focus on one miasm,. It is important to perceive each miasmatic state of the remedy, in order to understand the disease state, because then we become aware of how a person perceives and react to his surroundings, how he perceives himself and how he reacts when things became unmanageable and stressful. We need to understand the remedy as how it's related to the miasm. This understanding comes from study of the symptoms both physical and mental. The understanding of the mental delusions of a particular miasm in a remedy. The delusion of that remedy must lie in that particular miasm.

Example: Arsenic (syphlitic) despair of recovery, suicidal disposition, weakness, feels unloved, insecure.

*Arsenic (psoric)"delusion sees thieves"*

*Arsenic (sycotic) cannot trust people, obsessive, compulsive*

There are only a few remedies that belong to one miasm: psora-psorinum, sycosis- medorrhinum, syphilis- syphilinum. To study one remedy "syphlinum" is to study a syphlitic miasm. Or a syphilis characteristic.

Rubics - antisocial, abusive, indifferent to the future, hopeless despair of recovery, desperation, his efforts are lost of no use. The situation is beyond his capacity to salvage it, manic tendencies, manic religiousness, Manic washing hands, yet hopeless so compensates into antisocial behaviour. "I don't care" attitude, mind goes slow/paralyzed, desire to kill, all fascists, all anarchists and exploiters in history are the product of the syphlitic miasm, Napoleon, Christopher Columbus, Aedie Amin, Hitler. Will regard appropriate both the death of an individual, or an atom bomb explosion over an entire town. The pathologies are concerned with destruction, ulceration, poor reaction, it's as if the body and mind decided to destroy itself because it sees no hope. Syphilis itself is a taint which slowly destroys, with a difficult death. Syphilis in a mother's body shows itself in forms of habitual abortions. The foetus is already in a process of self-destruction. "I wish I had never been born". Once we can understand the miasmatic element in a person we can see the out come of the case with certainty.

Why is it necessary for a homeopath to know the chronic miasms? Some might say as long as one prescribes according to the law of similia he cures his cases. The important factor here is "so long as he selects the most similar remedy as possible." The fact is, we cannot select the most similar remedy possible unless we understand the phenomena of the acting miasm.

The true similia is always based on the existing miasm. It makes the difference between fighting the disease in the dark and in bright light when one knows the underlying principle that fathers the phenomena. If one has no knowledge of the laws of action and reaction, how can we watch the progress of a case without a definite knowledge of the disease forces (miasms) with their mysterious and persistent progressions. So, if we can know nothing about the traits and characteristics of our enemy, it's impossible to wage war against the disease.

Theses things Hahnemann wrote about in his theory of disease. The physician skilled in anti-miasmatic prescribing dips deeper into the case and applies an agent that has a deeper and closer relationship with the prevented life force. The results are always better. "The suffering of the immediate vital principle which animates the interior of our bodies, when it is morbidly disturbed, produces symptoms in the organism that are manifest"–Organon

A knowledge of all miasmatic phenomena would be a complete knowledge of all that is known as disease. Hahnemann discovered the miasms due to the fact these ailments kept coming back, year after year. Even with the correct remedy given, still no permanent cure. Hahnemann's proof of the existence was the persistency of these chronic diseases considering, diet, hygiene, health still a come-back in the disease constantly repeating itself. They seem to come from within the organism itself, from some peculiar dynamics within, from something that was deranged. Within the life-force itself, inherent, internal, pre-existing within the dynamics. Hahnemann wrote in a footnote in "chronic diseases" about the third book of Moses (Leviticus) where the word psora is mentioned, given to eruptive diseases. The miasms run through our history from the beginnings. (Greek = psora = itch).

When complicated suppressive drugs came about, the psora also became complicated. Drugs such as arsenic, quinine, mercury used to suppress ailments became used more frequently. Soon a more malignant manifestation presented itself in forms of epidemics. When suppression took place in an organism with two or more miasms present, all conditions magnified and intensified.

# Chapter 9

# The 7 Chakras & The Endocrine System

## Endocrine Glands

Each of endocrine glands has a dual function. First, they perceive sensory energies received through the respective chakras, and transmit these sensory impulses to the brain. Secondly, they regulate many, many different body functions through the production of hormones, which are released into the bloodstream. These two roles are, of course, closely interrelated. In some of the endocrine glands, the structural separation between the two different functions is quite distinct. In other cases, it is more subtle. The primary distinguishing characteristic between the two is that the sensory units tend to be much more heavily populated with receptor cells, and corresponding nerve fibres, while the hormonal units tend to involve a more extensive blood flow.

Within the endocrine system, there is a command structure that is hierarchical in nature. Although the Pituitary gland was for a long time considered to be the "master" gland of the endocrine system, more recent studies have demonstrated that the Pineal gland modulates certain activities of the Pituitary. The Pineal gland is indeed the "master" gland of the system, and the chain of command progresses sequentially downward through the body. This command structure is not strictly linear. For example, the Pineal influences the Hypothalamus, and the Hypothalamus influences the Pituitary, but the Pineal also influences the Pituitary directly.

Within medical science, the list of endocrine glands continues to grow. It was not too long ago that controversy still existed as to whether of not such glands as the Pineal and Thymus are truly part of the endocrine system. Unfortunately some of our medical research techniques are not yet very well refined. A typical approach in determining the function of a gland is to remove the comparable gland in a non-human animal, and see what happens. This is akin to determining the function of a steering wheel in an automobile by removing it, and then observe what happens when we drive down the road! Some of the endocrine glands discussed in this book, such as the Sinuses, are still not considered by medical science to be part of the endocrine system.

## The Chakras & the Endocrine

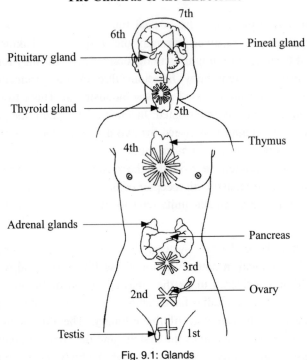

Fig. 9.1: Glands

# Description of the Endocrine Glands and the related Chakras

Following is a brief description of the nature and function of each of the endocrine glands, and the related chakra. A summary of this information is included in a table at the end of this section. This table may serve as a convenient frame of reference as one reads through the individual descriptions.

## Pineal Gland and Crown Chakra

Comparatively little is known within medical science regarding the Pineal gland. One reason for this is that it is located virtually in the center of the head, and is thus not easily accessible. Rene Descartes, the 17th-century French scientist-philosopher, believed the Pineal to be the "seat of the soul". It is becoming increasingly evident, he was very much on the right track.

The Pineal gland is located between, but just slightly above the brain stem and the Cerebellum. Its shape is similar to that of a small foot without the toes. It is suspended by a stalk, which corresponds to the manner in which an ankle is attached to a foot. Its size is slightly less than a half inch across the base of the foot. Functionally, it is divided into two segments. The anterior, or front part of the foot is involved with the hormonal functions. The posterior, or heel is associated with the sensory aspects. The internal layer of the heel is heavily populated with photoreceptor cells, very similar to those found in the retina of the eyes. The nerve fibres extending from these photoreceptor cells pass up through the stalk, and enter the Cerebellum through an anterior appendage known as the Corpora Quadrigemina. The Pineal gland is the only endocrine gland whose nerve fibres terminate in the Cerebellum, rather than the Cerebrum.

As indicated previously, the Pineal is the master gland in the command structure of the endocrine system. Thus, much of its work is accomplished through the other glands. The Pineal itself is known to secrete two hormone-like substances: melatonin and serotonin. Injections of melatonin are known to induce sleep. And during normal periods of sleep, the melatonin levels in the bloodstream have been found to be higher than during the waking state. Thus, it appears that the Pineal has a direct role related to the circadian rhythms of the body.

The Crown chakra is like an energy cone that extends upward from the top of the head. The focal point of the cone is directed downward, through the fontanel, to the Pineal. This chakra is able only to receive energies, not transmit energies. The Crown chakra, functioning in conjunction with the Pineal, is the *primary communication link between the soul and the brain.*

In the section entitled, "Soul and Oversoul Structures", it is indicated that at its essence level, an oversoul is actually a geometric structures, constructed of Light. The cumulative memory of the oversoul is stored gossamer-like filament within these structures of Light geometry. Information can thus be transmitted from the oversoul (or the soul) to the brain via the Crown chakra, in the form of patterns of light. The photoreceptors in the Pineal are sensitive to these light patterns, and convert them to nerve impulses, which are in turn transmitted to the cortex area of the Cerebellum.

Since the Crown chakra functions similar to an eye, and since it is the primary communication link between the soul-self and the human-self, this chakra is sometimes referred to as the "Eye of God". Similarly, in Egyptian mysticism, it is referred to as the "Eye of Horus".

In discussing the Pineal gland, we indicated that it is the "master gland" within the hierarchical command structure of the endocrine system. In like manner, the Crown chakra is intended to be the "master chakra". In other words, it is intended that the soul-self be master over the human-self. Unfortunately, in our humanness, we sometimes let some of our other chakras take charge.

## Hypothalamus Gland and Forehead Chakra

The Hypothalamus is a pair of glands which reside on the lower extremities of the Cerebral hemispheres, just under the Corpus

Callosum. Together they form the floor and side walls of the 3rd ventricle of the brain. They are thus in direct contact with the Cerebrospinal fluid system. The structure of the Hypothalamus includes very extensive nerve networks.

The chakra which is associated with the Hypothalamus extends outward from the center of the forehead, about an inch above the Brow chakra. It has not traditionally been recognized within metaphysical science, and thus has not been given a name. We have termed it the Forehead chakra simply because of its location.

The primary function of the Forehead chakra, working in conjunction with the Hypothalamus, it the *facility of mental telepathy*. Thought exists as *patterns of light*. Throughout history, some of the mystics (Light Workers) have been able to observe these "thought-forms" with their inner senses. There is a very interesting book by Annie Besant and C. W. Leadbeater which graphically depicts a variety of thought-forms which they have observed.

Within the Hypothalamus is a large population of photoreceptor cells, similar to those found in the Pineal. Like the Crown chakra, the thought-form patterns of light are received through the Forehead chakra, where they are directed to the photoreceptor cells of the respective Hypothalamus glands. These cells in turn translate the light patterns into nerve impulses which are sent on the cortex areas of the respective Cerebral hemispheres.

A fundamental difference between the Crown chakra and the Forehead chakra is that the Forehead chakra can transmit as well as receive. Thus, mental telepathy can function in both directions through the Forehead chakra and respective Hypothalamus glands.

In Germany, in 1924, Hans Berger was attempting to discover the nature of mental telepathy. In his efforts, he detected very low level electrical voltages present at various locations on the surface of the head. These voltages are oscillatory in nature, and are in the range of approximately 1 to 25 Hertz. This discovery launched the beginning of biofeedback research which has emerged much more actively during the past 3 decades. The primary focus of this research has been to correlate the frequency of these "brain waves" to the various states of conscious awareness. This frequency spectrum has been segmented into four bands, labelled *beta, alpha, theta, and delta;* in descending order of frequency. As a general rule, the lower end of the frequency spectrum is characterized by a lower level of conscious awareness. These brainwaves are closely related to the functioning of the Hypothalamus, and thus we know that the Hypothalamus plays an active role in controlling the states of consciousness. In our discussion of the Pineal, we indicated that through the secretion of melatonin, it influences the waking and sleeping states of the body. It now seems clear that the Pineal works in conjunction with the Hypothalamus to control the states of consciousness at a more refined level.

The so-called "mind-altering" drugs function through the pharmacology of Hypothalamus to artificially alter the states of consciousness. It is no wonder that overdoses of such drugs can virtually destroy some of the neuro-networks located in the Hypothalamus.

## Pituitary Gland and Brow Chakra

The Pituitary Gland, also known as the Hypophysis, is located just in front of the Pons, a unit of the brain stem, and is approximately a half inch in diameter. It is cradled within a cavity of the sphenoid bone in very much the same manner as an eyeball fits into an eye socket of the skull. Like the Pineal, it consists of two primary sections; a posterior (rear) lobe known as the *Neurohypophysis*, and an anterior (front) lobe known as the *Adenohypophysis*. The respective names provide an indication as to their function. *"Adeno-"* is a Greek derivative which corresponds to "gland". This is the section of the Pituitary which is associated with the hormonal functions of the endocrine system. *"Neuro"*, of course, relates to the nervous system. It is this function of the Pituitary that is the subject of our interest related to sensory receptors.

The Neurohypophysis connects directly to top of the brain stem via the Pituitary stalk. This stalk is filled with a bundle of nerve fibers which interconnect to the ganglia of the Hypothalamus. Similar to the Pineal, these nerve fibres originate in photoreceptor within the posterior wall of the Neurohypophysis, very much like the photoreceptors within the retina of the eye.

The Brow chakra extends outward toward the front from a point midway between the eye brows. The focal point of this chakra is directed inward toward the photoreceptor cells in the Pituitary. The Brow chakra, functioning in conjunction with the Pituitary, is traditionally referred to by mystics as the "third eye". Through the third eye, many Light Workers are able to perceive such things as the auric field of individuals, which appears as light of various colours surrounding the body. Since the Brow chakra is tuned to 5th dimensional energies, the third eye provides vision into the 5th dimension.

## Sinus Glands and Nasal Chakra

The Sinuses are essentially paired groups of cavities located in the vicinity of the nose and eyes. They are usually subdivided into four groups: frontal, ethmoidal, sphenoidal, and maxillary. The frontal sinuses are located immediately on each side of the third eye. The ethmoidal and sphenoidal are imbedded within the bone structure of the nasal cavity. And the maxillary, the largest of the group, and located just behind the cheek bones. The Sinuses which function as part of the endocrine-sensory system include and ethmoidal and maxillary subgroups.

The Sinuses are normally considered to be simply cavities, rather than glands. However, the interior walls of the Sinuses are covered with mucus membranes, which include sophisticated cell structures. The reason that they open to the nasal cavity is that their function requires access to the in-breathe of air. Embedded within the membrane structures on the interior walls of the Sinuses are chemoreceptor cells which sense particles suspended in the air that we breathe. This is why many people feel their Sinuses react when the air is full of pollens.

In recent years, there has been significant interest in the impact which the ionic content of air has on our overall attitude. Generally the negative ions are believed to have an exhilarating effect on our attitude, while the positive ions tend to cause depression. It is through the endocrine function of the Sinus glands that the ionic content is perceived and translated to hormonal releases which affect our attitude.

The chakra which functions in conjunction with the Sinus glands is another one of the chakras which has not yet been acknowledged by metaphysical science. Because of its location, we have termed it the "Nasal" chakra. To locate the two focal points of this chakra, one may place a finger on each side of the lower flange of the nose, and locate the gentle depressions in the bone structures which exist at those points. The nasal chakra extends outward toward the front of the face. It is one of the chakras that is capable of receiving energies, but not transmitting energies.

## Thyroid Gland and Throat Chakra

The Thyroid gland is located in the throat area. It is in the shape of an "H", folding around the front side of the trachea where it joins the lower part of the larynx. Thus there is a primary lobe of the Thyroid on each side of the trachea.

The Throat chakra functions in conjunction with the Thyroid gland. This chakra is bi-directional in that it extends outward toward front, and also outward toward the rear of the throat area. It also is able to both receive and transmit energies.

Within the two lobes of the Thyroid we find a very interesting cell structure. It consists of closely packed spherical-shaped "follicles", some of which are as much as one millimetre in diameter. The interior of these follicles is filled with a colloidal liquid, and the interior surface of the follicles has a profusion of minute hair-like extensions protruding into the liquid. This structural concept of hair-like protrusions into a liquid is also found within the Cochlea, which is the sensory unit of the inner ear. Within the mechanism of the ear, sound waves are translated into vibratory movements within the liquid, which in turn create slight movements of the hair-like projections. These in turn are translated into nerve impulses, which are transmitted to the brain.

Mystics have long associated the throat chakra with the function of clairaudience. The similarity of cell structures within the Thyroid and the inner ear certainly supports this notion.

Like the other endocrine glands, the Thyroid has an important role related to hormone secretions. However, our primary focus for this discussion is on its role as a sensory receptor.

## Thymus Cervical Extensions Glands and the High-Heart Chakra

The Thymus glands consist of two separate lobes which reside just above, and in contact with the heart. They are protected on the front side by the sternum. Although the left and right lobes of the Thymus are similar in function, they are not exactly symmetric with respect to each other, primarily because of their need to compensate for the lack of bilateral symmetry of the heart.

Attached to the upper extremity of each of the main Thymus lobes, is an elongated lobe which extends virtually to the lower extremity of the Thyroid glands. These have been considered to be simply extensions of the Thymus glands, and are referred to as the "cervical extensions". In actuality, however, these two extensions are a separate pair of glands, with functions that are distinct from the primary Thyroid glands. At some point in the future, when more is learned about their function, they will undoubtedly receive their own unique name.

Just as medical science has essentially ignored the Cervical Extensions, so also has metaphysical science ignored the associated chakra. This chakra is located where the Clavicle bones (collar bones) join the upper end (Manubrium) of the Sternum. For lack of a better term, we have elected to refer to this chakra as the High-Heart chakra.

Like the Throat chakra, it is bi-directional, and thus extends outward both toward the front and toward the rear of the body.

Although the hormonal functions of the Cervical Extensions have not yet been identified, one fact that is known is that there are a large number of nerve fibres which originate within the Cervical Extensions. These link into the sympathetic nervous system. We may thus assume that these glands, functioning in conjunction with the High-Heart chakra, perceive and transmit sensory impulses to the Cerebrum.

At this point I would like to indulge in some speculation which, I believe is well-founded. Let me begin with some background information.

A long time friend and mentor, Derald Langham, was a geneticist with a doctorate in both genetics and the humanities. Through his understanding of genetics, he evolved a general systems concept which he termed "Genesa". Under a microscope, he was able to observe how in the biological beginning of animal life, a sperm penetrates an ovum to form a single cell, or zygote. After a period of time, this zygote divides through a process of mitosis into 2 cells. The next step is that the 2 cells each divide laterally into two, making a total of 4 cells. The next step is that the 4 cells each divide into two along a third axis, making a total of 8 cells in the form of a cube. He observed this cube of 8 cells to be the fundamental building block of living forms. From that point on, the manner in which these basic building blocks link together to form a human, versus a dolphin or some other life form, is all based on the information contained in the respective genes. Derald firmly believed that our genes are under control of our mind, and that they can thus be altered.

In the human form, the original zygote is located near the focal point of the High-Heart chakra, which Derald termed the Genea- zero point. The embryo, and later the foetus build out all of the features of the human body from that point of origin, utilizing the blueprint contained in the genes.

In the Overview, we mentioned the mutations which are taking place in the DNA structures of our genes. It is my belief that these changes are being directed by intelligent impulses of energy received through our High-Heart chakra. These impulses are received by the receptor cells within the Cervical Extensions of the Thymus, where the information is translated into instructions for the pharmacology within the glands. I believe that it is this pharmacology which generates hormones and perhaps other substances which alter the *deoxyribonucleic acid* (DNA) and *ribonucleic acid* (RNA) within our genes.

Derald became intrigued with the geometry associated with a cube, since this seemed to be fundamental to the structure of life forms. This led him to the development of geometric structures which are related to geometric structures of our Light body. Derald observed that the geometric center of our Light body also coincides with the location of our original zygote, at the focal point of the High-Heart chakra.

## Thymus Glands and the Heart Chakra

It has only been within the past decade or so that the Thymus has received much attention within the medical community. In fact, some of the older reference book do not even list the Thymus glands as part of the endocrine system. But with the advent of AIDS, and other related disorders, the Thymus has attracted much interest in relation to the crucial role it plays in the immune system of the body.

The predominant cells within the interior of the Thymus are epithelial type receptor cells, which are similar in structure to the chemoreceptor cells in the taste buds of the tongue. Just as the Brow chakra corresponds to the sense of sight, and the Throat chakra corresponds to the sense of hearing; the Heart chakra seems to correspond to the sense of taste. Since the four primary sensations involved in taste are sweet, sour, salt, and bitter; it is interesting to ponder the possibility that there may be correspondences between these four sensations and the feelings which we experience through the Heart chakra.

Like the Throat and High-Heart chakras, the Heart chakra is bi-directional, extending both toward the front and the rear of the body. It is capable of both receiving energies and transmitting energies.

As indicated previously, the Thymus glands have attracted considerable interest in recent years because of their role related to the immune system of the body. It is interesting to note that some of the therapists, such as Louise Hay, who are having success in helping to strengthen the immune system, focus primarily on learning to feel more love for oneself. The focal point for our experience of love, and other related feelings, resides within the heart chakra.

## Adrenal Glands and the Solar Plexus Chakra

The Adrenal glands are a pair of glands which also are sometimes referred to as the Suprarenal glands. One is located on the top of each kidney. Each gland, in itself, consists of two segments. The outer portion is known as the *"cortex"*, and the inner portion is referred as the *"medulla"*.

The cortex is involved primarily with the pharmacology aspects of the gland, and produces a family of substances known as steroids. Unfortunately, steroids are probably best known for their inappropriate artificial use by some athletes to enhance muscle building. The Adrenal glands also are well known for their production of adrenaline. Adrenaline energizes the muscles of the body, and especially the muscles of the circulatory and digestive systems.

The medulla is the portion of the Adrenal gland which is involved in the sensory function. It is heavily populated with chromaffin nerve cells, which are connected into the spinal nerve system via the Celiac ganglion. This ganglion is located in the area of the body generally known as the Solar Plexus. The chromaffin nerve cells are essentially chemoreceptor cells, which have similarity to the chemoreceptor cells found in the olfactory glands.

The Adrenal glands function in conjunction with the Solar Plexus chakra. Like the Throat and Heart chakras, the Solar Plexus chakra is bi-directional, extending outward toward the front and the rear of the body. The Solar Plexus chakra also can both receive and transmit energies.

It is sometimes through colloquial expressions that we gain insights into various aspects of our human experience. We sometimes hear the expression, "I have a gut feeling that ...". This would seem to be a way of expressing a feeling derived through the Solar Plexus chakra, and related Adrenal sensory system; a feeling that may not necessarily be supported by the rationale of the conscious mind. Another colloquialism that we occasionally hear when one perceives that something is awry is the expression, "I smell a rat!" Or if we are going to check our feelings about a situation, we sometimes say that we are going to "smell out the situation". This expressions would seem to be an unconscious acknowledgement of the similarity between our sense of smell, and our perceptions derived through the Solar Plexus and related Adrenal sensory receptors.

## Sexual Glands and the Sexual Chakra

As we have considered the various glands of the endocrine system, a consistent pattern has emerged. In each case, there is one section of the gland that is involved primarily with the *hormonal* functions of the endocrine system, and there is another section that is involved with the *sensory* aspects. This is true whether it is a singular gland, such as the Pituitary, or a pair of glands, such as the Thyroid, Thymus, and Adrenal. In some cases the structural separation of these two functional units within a gland is quite distinct, and in other cases it is much more subtle. In no case is the separation as distinct as it is in the sexual glands.

Reference books on the endocrine system normally list only the *gonads* in conjunction with the sexual glands. The gonads consist of the paired *testicles* in the male, and the paired *ovaries* in the female. However, the gonads are only that aspect of the sexual glands which are involved in the hormonal and reproductive aspects. The sensory aspects of the sexual glands are incorporated into the *genitalia;* or more specifically, the *penis* in the male, and the *clitoris* in the female. Thus, the sexual glands are unique compared to the other glands of the endocrine system, in that the hormonal function involves *paired* glands, and the sensory function involves only a *singular* gland.

As is well known, the tip of the penis and the clitoris is heavily populated with tactile-receptor nerve cells. These nerves connect into the spinal nerve system via the Mesenteric ganglion, which is located in the lumbar region of the spine.

The sexual glands function in conjunction with the Sexual chakra. Like the Heart and Solar Plexus chakras, the Sexual chakra is bi- directional, and can both receive and send energies.

## Base Chakra

The Base chakra has an important function related to the Sacrum, and more specifically to the so-called Kundalini energy. However, it is not involved in the sensory aspects of our human experience in the same manner as the other chakras of our body.

## Chakras and Related Endocrine-Sensory Glands

| Chakra | Gland | Function | Receptor Type |
|--------|-------|----------|---------------|
| Crown | Pineal | Intuition | Photo |
| Forehead | Hypothalamus | Mental Telepathy | Photo |
| Brow | Pituitary | Clairvoyance | Photo |
| Nasal | Sinus | Attitude | Chemo |
| Throat | Thyroid | Clairaudience | Kinetic |
| High-Heart | Cervical Extension | Intention | Chemo |
| Heart | Thymus | Taste | Chemo |
| Solar Plexus | Adrenal | Smell | Chemo |
| Sexual | Gonads | Touch | Tactile |

# Chapter 10
# Colour Energy is Colour Healing

The use of colour in healing goes back 5000 years, Chinese, Egyptians, Greek, Tibetans and native Americans just to name a few. Stones and crystals were used for healing and to enhance power of kings queens and other world leaders.

Colour affects the body in many ways:

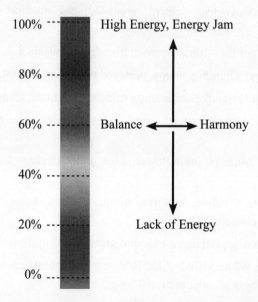

Fig. 10.1: Colour effects on body (Refer Plate IV for Colour picture)

In the womb the eyes started out as part of the endocrine system and brain. As we develop and grow the different parts of the eyes stay connected to the different glands so by looking at different colours it stimulates the glandular secretion that affects the glands assigned to different functions of the body. For an example: looking at the colour blue stimulates the thyroid and that affect your heart, bones, hair and reproductive organs.

Colour moves us on a subtle or subconscious level. Look at the colour *red* link it moves us to action. Why do you think McDonalds uses Red and Yellow in their marketing of their food? Those colours attract us and move us to action!

Our language also speaks in colour:

Seeing *red*, (anger), I feel *blue* (sad), sunshine makes us happy (*yellow*), what is the colour of money? *Green* the other side of green is green with envy.

*Colours that move us:*

**Red:** Movement, centerd, grounded, can manifest abundance, vitality.

**Orange:** Emotions, creative, friendly, enthusiasm.

**Yellow:** Thinking, happy, personal power, intelligent, analytical.

**Green:** Friendly, community minded, balanced, team building.

**Blue:** Verbal activity, trust, calm, polite, detailed, patient, inspiring.

**Navy blue:** Intuition power, wise, understanding, fulfilled, high ethics.

**Violet:** Creative, intuitive, divine wisdom, knowingness, and universal consciousness.

**Turquoise:** Balanced blue and green, coming from the heart.

**Pink:** White & Red=Pink; Bringing the highest spiritual thoughts into the physical, unconditional love.

**White:** Is all colours balanced.

**Gold:** Masculine power.

**Silver:** Feminine power.

| What to wear when closing a deal? | Red & navy |
|---|---|
| What to wear when prospecting? | Blue, navy, red, yellow |
| What to wear when you want to be calm? | Blue, violet, indigo |
| Having trouble sleeping? | Navy (indigo) sheets to help calm the mind |

Different ways to get the energy without wearing it : Drink lemon water for yellow or beets for red; calm the mind blue berries.

I know, it is a little imprudent to write in such a shallow way on such a large and comprehensive topic as colour and the importance of colour on all living organisms. However, one should know something about how colours work and in what way you may use colours to better your health both physically and psychologically.

Many people have written books on colour : Sir Isaac Newton, Johann Wolfgang von Goethe, Faber Bitten, Rudolf Steiner, and hundreds of contemporary authors. They have all introduced the same idea in the best way : Colour is energy. Book stores have hundreds of books on this theme and if, after having read this introduction, you are interested in learning more about colour, I would recommend you go to the nearest book store. But now I would like to tell you a little about colour and light.

Colour is more than decoration and pleasure to our eyes. It is light - light split into different wave lengths, vibrating at different speeds and frequencies. An object that absorbs all wavelengths and does not reflect any is called black - and an object that reflects everything is white. Between black and white lies our colour world. Colours are wavelengths of energy that to us appear as colours because of the potential and capability of the object to either absorb or reflect the energy. This is how we experience colour. An apple is red because it absorbs all colours except red. Red also has the longest wavelength of all the colours.

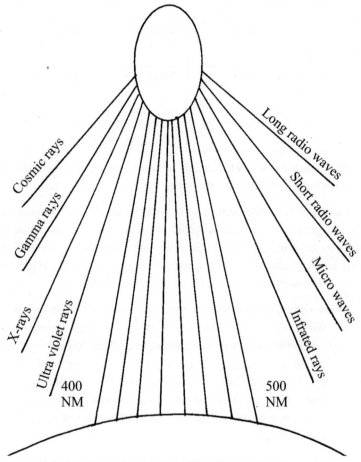

Fig. 10.2: Colours wavelenghts (Refer Plate IV for Colour picture)

The strangest thing is that scholars ignore the colour energies and do nothing with the most exciting and beautiful things we have in front of our eyes - but they have accepted the short and long wavelengths on either side of the visible colour spectrum.

# Colour Energy and the Chakra

We have chosen to use the Sanskrit word chakra - chakra is the most frequently used and descriptive word for energy points or whirls of energy. The chakra points do not exist in our physical body but in our etheric body. Here the cosmic energy enters and connects our body with the energy coming from the earth. These energy whirls are in contact with our physical body through points explained as:

| | |
|---|---|
| Crown chakra | Violet energy |
| Brow/Third Eye chakra | Blue energy |
| Throat chakra Heart chakra | Green energy |
| Solar Plexus chakra | Yellow energy |
| Spleen chakra | Orange energy |
| Root chakra | Red energy |

These points are what it is all about - either physically, mentally, emotionally, or spiritually. If these points are healthy and in balance, then we are healthy. It is important when you are going to transfer energy from one chakra to another that you know what colour is the complementary colour, i.e. with what colour you may be adjusted.

| Colour | Complementary Colour |
|---|---|
| Red | Blue |
| Orange | Indigo |
| Yellow | Violet |
| Green | Red |
| Blue | Red |
| Indigo | Orange |
| Violet | Yellow |

We are born with the opportunity to make use of all colour energies, and we develop according to a colour scale - from birth in the palest pink, to red in puberty, and as years pass by and experience comes, towards the violet in old age. Our aim should be to leave this life in beautiful pastel shades with a tinge of white and gold.

At any rate, man is a beautiful and fascinating sight to people who can see through other eyes other than those with which we have been taught to see.

The colour energies that surround us are an ever changing picture of sparkling colours, which reflect how we are inside ourselves. Everything from physical health to emotional and mental circumstances show through the colours of our aura.

When all our chakras are in balance, we display all the colours of the rainbow clearly and evenly. If there are disturbances on any level this shows in our chakras. This means that the energies do not flow evenly and smoothly along our spine-something is wrong. And what can we do about it?

First of all we are concerned with balance - being balanced. Throughout our whole life we must strive for balance - train and exercise so that the body may be harmonized mentally, emotionally, and physically. Colour energy works both in a positive and a negative way. By knowing ourselves and our positive and negative sides we may achieve balance by adding more energy of same colour or by adding another colour energy (usually the complementary colour). For example, a person who has a lot of the red energy dominating her/his being and who admits that in some situations she/he becomes more and more hot-headed, arrogant, and domineering, would tune down her/his unbalanced chakra with energies from the green colour. Go for a walk in the woods, take a green bath, put on a green sweater, and eat more green foods. On the whole, try to dampen the negative red energy-bring it into balance. In the opposite case, a person who in her/his daily life leads an introverted, closed up life with self-pity and little gratitude for her/his existence, needs the red energy. By using colour more consciously these apparently small changes could be the little extra you need to help yourself out of a situation you are unable to manage. Many unnecessary deeds and happenings might he avoided if you are in balance. Remember there are actually no really bad human qualities, but there are unbelievably many unbalanced people. Use colours and get to know yourselves-be conscious of how you use colours and why-ask yourself why there are certain colours you don't like.

## Life Power and Life Energy – Red

The root chakra at the bottom of the spine is governed by the red energy. This power center is closely connected with the earth. It governs all our earthly life and is the outgoing, positive, "yes to life" attitude. It is important that the root chakra be earth grounded. Fatigue, fear, and anxiety are often caused by the missing contact with earth reality. All goals that were never accomplished - the missing consequence from theory to practice are caused by the lack of the red energy. The missing security and trust in ourselves and our worth are often caused by not being loyal and true to ourselves. To start self-aid and the understanding of the red energy we should place our feet firmly on the ground, and look at ourselves and others with love. The strongest red energy is the power of reproduction, and this is probably the energy we know the best. The warm, red sexual energy sets the root chakra spinning. The vibrations increase as the energy moves up towards the heart chakra and the throat chakra, finally to give us an experience of the yin-yang balance - the mutual dependence and belonging in love of all things, actually satisfying both the physical and mental. The red energy also is the power that provides the creative energy on all levels. Everything that is to be commenced - all pioneering work needs the life vitality of red.

**Physically** the root chakra energizes the feet, the legs, the tail bone, the vagina, the urinary organs, and the adrenal glands.

**Mentally** this energy gives power to the strong life qualities of courage, self-confidence, security, positive love, and will-power.

## Red

In using red in baths as well as in clothes, red foods, or interiors it should be remembered that what we are striving for is balance. This energy must not be misused, and red energy is not enough to live on or for. This is the energy you need to help the other chakras to function in accordance with each other. Too much or too little of any colour is just as bad. The key word is balance.

## The Positive Sides of Red

Courageous – strong will
Spontaneous – honest
Grateful – forgiving
Humanistic – extrovert

## And the Negative

Domineering – arrogant
Self-pitying – self-indulging
Quick-tempered – impolite
Passionate – brutal

## Red energy may help when:

You feel tired and indisposed
You are anaemic
You are cold
You need courage and self-confidence
You are starting a cold
You need the warmth that increases your vital energies
You have poor blood circulation

## You should not use red when:

You are emotionally out of balance
You are angry and excited
You have infectious wounds
You have a heart problem (take a pink bath instead)

On the whole you should be careful with the red bath - there is a strong power in the red energy. Small children should not be bathed in red water. However, difficult or restless children may benefit from a pink or rose bath.

## Affirmation

"Let the red energy flow through my veins and provide me with new life and courage to do everything I have to do."

## Red Tips

Red is a good colour in playrooms as it increases excitement and physical activity - but it also increases passion. Red in a place of work where risk handling takes place is not advisable. Accidents may occur where red is in the picture. Red should be used where activity should be increased, but not where peace and concentration should prevail.

## Red in clothes

With red we show a vital and somewhat passionate image of independence. But the person may often seem a little aggressive.

## Red Foods

If you should want more red energy you may eat foods like beets, radishes, red cabbage, watercress, spinach, meat, cayenne pepper, tomatoes, strawberries, cherries, and all red-skinned fruits.

## The Astrological Sign and Planet for Red

The astrological sign Aries is red, and the planet is Mars.
*Tuesday is a red day.*

# Life Power and Life Energy – Orange

## Constructive Joy

People who like the orange colour love life. Many people do not like the orange colour, but we all need this energy. Orange is the best stimulant and help in times of depression, loneliness, and boredom - on the whole it is the best emotional stimulant.

Joy comes from deep within and we all need joy - the orange energy helps bring out this joy. The orange colour has the love from the red and the wisdom from the yellow. It strengthens your confidence and independence.

"We are what we think" has a lot to do with the orange energy, as it governs health and vitality. "A sound mind is a sound body" is an expression that fits the orange colour. Balance is important here as the misuse of food, stimulants in any form, all luxury, belong under the domain of the spleen chakra. Extreme indulgence or asceticism-be it in food, sex, sports activities - all this shows a chakra out of balance. Vegetarians for instance, need the orange energy.

## Physically

The spleen chakra gives energy to the bronchia, chest diseases, disturbances in the spleen, kidney ailments, and gall stone problems. It increases the intake of oxygen, helps lungs, and releases flatulence from the stomach.

## Mentally

The spleen chakra gives energy to remove suppression and inhibitions-it helps expand one's horizon and create new ideas. Like the red energy it gives courage and power to tackle everyday problems.

## Orange

In using orange one can learn to understand how the stomach tells us about our situation. We all know the butterfly feeling or the heavy sinking feeling before something is going to take place. The stomach often gives us the first warning when something is wrong, for instance an infection. If our spleen chakra is in balance we are able to enjoy our existence-take life as it is without asking for more than we can handle. Children often have a fine orange energy. They have the ability to enjoy themselves spontaneously and enjoy their play. If you have too much red in the orange this may make you angry and inconsiderate. Too much yellow in the orange may make you querulous and impossible to live with. You may have a nervous stomach if you cannot control your feelings. But if there is an excess of orange, one is easily affected by what other people feel or **mean**; one forgets to be oneself in a wish to satisfy other people.

## The Positive sides of Orange
Joy-enthusiasm
Independent-sociable
Fond of food-energetic
Sporty, occupied with health
Self- assured-constructive

## And the Negative
Proud-destructive
Let other people clear things up
Exhibitionist
Bulimia
Misuse of alcohol

## Orange Energy may help when:
You have chronic eczema
You lack working spirit
You have skin problems
You have asthma
You want to increase your appetite
You have allergies
You have vertical grooves on your nails
You need a refreshing start to your day-take an orange bath
You need to bring out the joy you have  inside you, and you need to have a feeling of well being

## Affirmation
"Let the orange energy fills me with happiness and vitality - I feel alive and well."

## Orange Tips

Orange colour in a room will give physical energy from the active vibrations of the red and intellectual vibrations from the yellow. Orange is also fine in a room where you wish to gather family and friends, and in a room where you want to read and study. It energizes creative spontaneous ideas. However, too much orange may cause self-pity.

## Orange in Clothes

With orange clothes you express sincere joy and interest in other people. You seem thoughtful and caring. However, too much orange and you may seem insecure, too modest, self-pitying, and dependent on others.

## Orange Foods

Oranges, apricots, peaches, melons, mangos, carrots, mandarins.

## The Astrological Sign and Planet for Orange

Red/Orange sign is Taurus, and the planet is Venus.
Orange sign is Gemini, and the planet is Mercury.
Yellow/Orange sign is Cancer, and the planet is the Moon
*Wednesday is an orange day*

# Knowledge and Wisdom – Yellow

The golden yellow energy is related to wisdom; wisdom in thoughts, words and deeds. The solar plexus chakra is often called the brain of the nervous system and is the most critical point of all vitalization points in the body. When we are stressed for instance, we either eat too much or we cannot stand food at all. If your solar plexus is in balance, you should not suffer from ulcers, gall stones, catarrh of the large intestine or diabetes. These illnesses show that there are problems with your feelings, anything from showing feelings to controlling them. A well balanced solar plexus chakra shows a person who is open and spontaneous, who can laugh or cry, be nervous and afraid; a person who can be herself/himself in all situations or moods. People might then say that this type of person does not seem in harmony, and that she/he is uncontrolled or unstable - however it is more important to be oneself - not to control oneself to the extent of appearing to be another type of person. You should be happy as the person you are and always strive towards balance. If too much red is introduced into the yellow, one may lean towards more than a usual interest in: money, possessing property, and security. If too much orange is introduced into the yellow there may be more interest in sex, food, and drugs. These are usually the trials we have here on earth - but if we are able to balance ourselves in this respect, we have come quite far in our evolution.

## Physically

Yellow gives energy to digestion, constipation, flatulence in the intestines, liver problems, diabetes, and skin problems. The yellow energy may help cleanse billions of pores in the skin.

## Mentally

Yellow gives clarity of thought. It gives good ideas and increases awareness. It has a powerful effect on the nervous system and it helps left brain operations such as reading and writing. Yellow stimulates the use of words and imagination. The yellow energy is good for children as it enhances children's ability to perceive and understand.

## Yellow

By using too much yellow one may get diarrhoea and sleeplessness. Mentally ill people may become very irritated with yellow. This colour should not be used in mental institutions.

## The Positive Sides of Yellow

Good-humoured
Optimistic
Confident
Clear thoughts
Wide horizons

## And the Negative
Likes flattery
Excesses
Pessimistic
Sly
Cowardly
Skeptical

## Yellow Energy may help when:
You feel nervous or tired
You are dissatisfied
You are melancholic or a little sad
You have flatulence
You have skin diseases
You have poor digestion
You have parasites
You have weight problems (either too little or too much)
Yellow is a wonderful brain stimulant

## You Should not use Yellow when:
You are suffering from a nervous strain or have problems.

## Affirmation
"Let the yellow energy fill me with sunshine - let God's love and wisdom flow through my body and soul."

## Yellow Tips
Libraries and reading rooms function well in a yellow colour, but some green and violet in the interior will also help the concentration. Too much yellow creates restlessness. Yellow may also be used anywhere in the house where you want pleasant and happy surroundings, or in a room where you entertain your guests.

## Yellow in Clothes

With yellow clothes you express optimism and self-confidence that attracts other people. Like sunshine you may display your personality. Your expression is on a mental level, and you may also seem restless or overdo your activities.

## Yellow Foods

Yellow peppers, grapefruit, corn, melons, bananas, lemons, pineapples, eggs, olive oil, coffee, yellow squash, prunes.

## The Astrological Sign and Planet for Yellow

The astrological sign is Leo, the planet is the Sun.

The Yellow/Green is connected with Virgo, and the planet is Mercury. *Sunday is a yellow day.*

# Devotion and Love – Green

Green is the harmonizing and balancing energy. It has a strong influence on the heart and blood supply. If you have been through tough times you may not feel for the green colour energy. The green colour has a lot to do with the way you feel about yourself. The green colour is associated with abundance, and those who like green are often great givers. Green is connected with money, which in itself is an energy. What we do with this energy may be compared with "as you give you shall receive."

We also talk about people with green thumbs who have a knack for making everything grow. Contact with nature is very important if you want to be in balance and have a peaceful and harmonious life. One thing you can do if you feel uncomfortable and void of the green energy, is to go out into the woods or to the park. Find a tree and stand with your back to its trunk. Put your left arm behind you around the tree trunk and your right arm over your solar plexus. Breathe in deeply and ask the tree to give you energy - remember to thank the tree before you leave. Try this and you will find out that it works.

If you notice you are using a lot of green in your clothes and that you surround yourself with a lot of green, you may harbour a lot of anxiety that you are not fully aware of. Try to change the colours, bring in some warmer colours. Red is the complementary colour to green and may be good in this situation. Yellow might not be so good. We all have a need of expressing ourselves, but if we exaggerate the green we may easily become too moralizing, and put ourselves on a pedestal. You may like to impress people and may rather want to be admired than loved.

## Physically

Green gives energy to the heart, lungs, bronchia, arms and hands and the secondary circulation system.

## Mentally

Green gives a feeling of renewal, of new life, freshness and clarity. This colour also governs not only the physical heart but also the emotions. Heart attacks often happen because of a fear or dread of giving, a fear of being involved in anything, or a fear of being hurt. An offended and hurt green person who feels he has lost face may also get stomach troubles. If such emotional feelings and problems are not solved and extend over a longer period of time, hypertension and a heart attack may be the result. The heart is the center of the soul and it is the heart that makes us fellow-beings, but the most important thing is that love is the leading principle of life. When we are together with family and friends we strengthen the heart energy. Having children also develops the heart center. We have to accept and love our children how they are, and for what they are. We help them on their own terms and love them without expecting anything in return. We should do the same with all our fellow-beings. When our heart center is in balance we are able to give positive feelings and happiness, unconditionally to everybody.

## The Positive Sides of Green
Harmonic
Loves children and animals
Understanding
Self-controlled
Adaptable
Sympathetic and compassionate
Generous and humble

## And the Negative
Lack of discrimination
Dishonest with money
Holds on to possessions
Jealous
Reckless
Stingy and cruel

## Green Energy may help when:
You need to soothe your nerves
You have a headache
You feel you need to balance yourself for peace and harmony
You have chronic diseases
You need to calm down before an important meeting
You have digestive problems

## Affirmation
"Let the green energy flow through my heart and give me peace and harmony in body and soul."

## Green Tips
Green is a good colour for bedrooms and kitchens. For example, you may want to keep a lot of green plants in the kitchen. However, in a room where you are working with mental creativity, green is not so good. In workshops where people are working in putting thoughts into practice, green is a good colour.

## Green in Clothes

When you are wearing a lot of green clothes it gives the impression of stability, tradition, and practical sense. You look down to earth and seem efficient and positive. Too much green and you will seem stiff and not very agile. You will seem analytical and not imaginative when it comes to original thoughts.

## Green Foods

Avocados, beans, broccoli, cucumber, all salads, peas, green squashes.

## The Astrological Sign and Planet for Green

Green sign is Libra, and the planet is Venus.
Blue/Green sign is Scorpio, the planets are Mars and Pluto.
*Friday is a green day.*

# Words and Knowledge – Blue

With the blue energy we move away from the physical level onto the more spiritual aspects of life. In so much as, the sky and the ocean gives us the feeling that life is an endless process. The truth about life becomes more and more clear when we get in contact with our own inner self.

Blue is a peaceful and relaxing colour that soothes tired nerves and alleviates the agony and pain we might suffer through physical stress. It has a pacifying effect on the nervous system and brings great relaxation. Despite its calming effect blue is also stimulating, but in a more spiritual level where it is truly uplifting. The nature of the blue energy is to connect human beings with the cosmic universe.

Blue is the colour of the soul, and blue is the colour of the greatest healing power in the world. Blue connects us with the higher power inside of us all. The soul knows the meaning of life, why we are on earth, and the task we are going to complete in our lifetime. Blue is the colour of purity and those who like blue like beauty in any form. Blue is also the most antiseptic colour energy in the world. The light from the colour is cool and electric. It soothes the eyes and mind. While red is expanding, blue is contracting and calms things down. The colour blue may enable the body to fight infectious diseases.

## Physically

Blue gives energy to problems caused by haemorrhoids, warts, climate, and trauma. Active children should do their homework in blue light. The throat chakra is governed by the blue energy. Blue energizes the throat, as it is through the throat we express ourselves - words carry power. Thus, the blue energy is connected with sound and the voice. All teachers, university professors, politicians, actors, singers, sergeants in the army, and anyone who uses their voice in a loud and clear way to express themselves, are using the blue energy.

## The Positive Sides of Blue

Fidelity
Loyal
Tactful
Affectionate
Inspiring
Inventive

## And the Negative

Ambitious
Disloyal/perfidious
Lack of faith
Suspicious
Apathetic
Snobbish
Emotionally unstable

## Blue Energy may help when:

You need to calm your mind and nerves
You have throat problems
You have had bites, bruises or itching
You cannot sleep
You have menstruation problems
You have problems with ears, eyes, nose or throat
You have had a shock
You have a fever-put your feet in a tub of blue water

## Affirmation

"Let the blue energy flow through me so that I may give out all that I learn.'

## Blue Tips

Blue is a calming colour and like the colour of green is fine for rooms meant for rest and relaxation. It is a good colour for your bedroom. The expansive expression of the blue colour makes small rooms seem larger and more diffusive.

Singing in the bath really has a fantastic cleansing effect. Water helps cleanse the etheric body and sound will loosen any negative vibrations in the atmosphere that surrounds you. Just don't repeat a Mantra in the bath as it is not safe to bring yourself into a hypnotic state while sitting in the bathtub.

## Blue in Clothes

In using blue colours in your clothes you show that you have the ability to diversify. It also has a calming effect. You seem competent and able to tackle any situation. With blue you seem interested in change, freedom, and progress. But with too much blue, it may often seem as if you think you are not tied by ordinary standards of proper behaviour.

## Blue Foods

Plums, blueberries, bramble berries, fish, asparagus, potatoes.

## The Astrological Sign and Planet for Blue

The astrological sign is Sagittarius, and the planet is Jupiter.
*Thursday is a blue day.*

# The Third Eye – Indigo

The brow chakra, often called "the third eye" is a very important energy center. Through this chakra you may withdraw into yourself. Many people withdraw to obtain peace and quiet, and freedom to stretch boundaries- for example, in meditation. Some people withdraw too much - and people with mental problems might prefer not to return to the physical world with all its demands - they feel this physical world is too demanding and aggressive. But there again, balance is the important thing. When you use this colour energy correctly you may be able to use your inner space as a retreat. This will help you to see things from a better and more experienced angle. All intuitive energies may be found here as well as all reincarnation experiences. In the indigo energy lies the understanding of the life process and the need to serve mankind. It gives energy to seekers of beauty, justice, and love. Some people accuse this energy of being unrealistic, but thanks to people of this energy, all reforms are brought into life. Indigo people are the great truth seekers; the people who teach through their own example. There is a saying "As we seek we shall find." When we obtain contact with the indigo ray and its vibrations, we will better understand the meaning of our lives, and we will learn to accept what we cannot change. Because, it is through accepting and letting locked situations go that things get better. It is through losing something that we find something. As all colour energies have positive and negative effects, we may look at how the negative energies work. The indigo energy should serve the universe with a helping and comforting spirit. However, if negatively balanced, one will withdraw and live in solitude, and refuse to take part in the life process and to take responsibility for one's own self.

These people become cynical, intolerant, ruthless, and no longer capable of helping themselves or others.

## Physically

Indigo gives energy to the pineal gland, which is linked to the nervous system, mental abilities, and the psychic potential in every human being. The organs of the senses, such as sight and hearing, are also under the influence of the indigo energy.

## Mentally

Indigo energy does not only help cleanse the bloodstream, but it also has a cleansing effect on the finer nerve functions. It has a psychological balancing influence on fear, frustrations, and distortions of inner energy is most important.

## The Positive Sides of Indigo

Intuitive
Fearless
Fulfilment of one's duty
Practical
Idealistic
Very active in one's surroundings

## And the Negative

Fear
Intolerant
Impractical
Judging
Sees only the dark sides
Melancholy

## Indigo Energy may help when:

You have problems sleeping
You need to calm down your nerves and your lymphatic system

You have problems with hearing
You have skin problems
You need to get into balance with the indigo energy

## Affirmation

"Let the indigo energy connect me with knowledge and understanding that I may receive help in my everyday life."

## Indigo Tips

Indigo strengthens and inspires intuition, thus the colour may be used in any place where creative work is to be done. It may be fine in a room where family problems and daily situations are to be discussed. Indigo is not a colour for larger areas, but more a colour to be used in a room for its good influences and effects.

## Indigo in Clothes

By wearing indigo clothes you show that you have an unconventional way of being. You seem individualistic and radical. You show that you are interested in others and new ideas with a philosophical and universal background.

## Indigo Foods

Eggplants, broccoli, blue grapes and other foods of the blue and violet colours.

## The Astrological Sign and Planet for Indigo

The astrological sign is Capricorn, and the planet is Saturn.
*Saturday is an indigo day.*

# Art and Beauty – Violet

The crown chakra has little physical energy and little contact with the earth. The crown chakra governs the energies to the pituitary gland and the hair. Most people have little relation to this energy and how they could use its potential. But people who have learnt how to train and use their intuition, will discover the fantastic potential of the crown chakra and its violet energy. Through the crown chakra we may obtain a connection with everything that is divine; with dead or living souls; and with spiritual helpers, of human or non-human origin, that we actually have and who are around us to help us. With the violet energy we have the possibilities and gifts that reach far beyond the physical planes. We may experience our existence as an integrated part of the spiritual universe. From this energy is created the inspiration that makes authors, healers, and all other people who express and bring through the divine power. The violet ray is the energy over all the other energies, and has the most intense electrochemical power. Violet has a sour flavour. The extreme blue violet energy is very stimulating to the nervous system. It has a cleansing power and inspires the spiritual nature. It stimulates the highest human ideals in art, music, poetry, and all others kinds of art. The famous artist and scientist of colour, Leonardo da Vinci, said that our power will increase tenfold if we meditated under the violet stained glass windows in the cathedral. When light shines through violet coloured glass, it provides us with the highest energies.

However, since violet has the highest vibrational speed of all colours, not everybody can utilize this colour. Many people avoid this colour and say they do not like it. This is probably because this energy cleanses the thoughts and emotions. All who are not of a creative nature would feel frustrated or even feel ill at ease in violet surroundings and light. But if we are in balance and are connected to the violet energy, the whole world is actually open to us.

## Physically

The colour violet gives energy to the spleen and lymphatic system activities. It helps kill bacteria and heals skin rashes.

## Mentally

From ancient times violet has been known to be the colour of spirit. It enhances spiritual power and creativity. It is the colour of the first aid box of metaphysics. But it is not the colour for a beginner in meditation.

# The Positive Sides of Violet

Great mental strength
Inspirational leader's
Kindly and just
Humanitarians
Self-sacrificing
Pure idealism

## And the Negative

Feel superior
Arrogant
Snobbish
Disloyal
Fanatic
Interest in black magic

## Violet Energy May Help When:

You have emotional problems
You feel that you need to clear the situation you are in
You feel that you need to strengthen your creativity
You feel that you need to strengthen your spiritual values

## You Should not use Violet when:

You are depressed or totally out of balance - use green instead.

## Affirmation

"Let the violet energy flow through me and cleanse my body to give
new life and new energy.

## Violet Tips

The over use of violet may express a tendency towards not accepting
things as they seem to be. A library or classroom would benefit from
this colour. Use violet in a playroom if the aim is to develop the

child's creativity. It would also be excellent in a theatre and other areas where one wishes to develop the imagination.

But again there must be a balance, with too much violet one would easily escape from reality into a fantasy world too often. Violet in a room where you entertain guests is not a good idea as it stops conversation and creates a craving for alcohol and drugs.

## Violet in Clothes

With violet clothes we provide an image of an unconventional and idealistic person. To some people violet indicates the dreamer, the mystique, and the lonely thinker. To others violet is an expression of the "New Age".

## Violet Foods

Eggplants, broccoli, blue grapes and all the blue foods, as found under the blue and indigo.

## The Astrological Sign and Planet for Violet

The astrological sign is Aquarius, and the planets are Saturn and Uranus.

Red/Violet is connected with Pisces, and the planets are Jupiter and Neptune.

*Monday is a violet day.*

# Chapter 11

# Balancing Chakra Centers through Colours Energy

## Part I

These questions are connected to your Red Root chakra power.

The Root chakra is your main power station and it is connected to your physical vitality and endurance, mental perseverance and it is the center that gives you your life's passion. The root center is also your connection to your existence.

### Issues to review are:

1. Are you physically fit?
2. Was there or is there currently any abuse (physical or verbal) in your life?
3. Are you able to put your thoughts into action?
4. Do you accomplish most of your goals?
5. Are money and a home very important to you?
6. Have you had any recent thoughts of self-destruction?

### Ways to bring in the RED energy and boost your Root chakra power are:

- Incorporate physical activities such as an exercise program or yoga
- Eat red foods and consume red drinks

- Use aromatherapy oils such as sandalwood, ylang ylang or juniper (consult a specially trained aromatherapist or aura counsellor to find the right oils for your specific chakra needs). Note: Every therapeutic oil or essence has its own healing power that can help with specific issues relating to each chakra
- Stimulating music with deep beats such as drums or music that makes your body move like Latin American music
- Wear or carry a red gemstones. Red stones would be Red Tiger's Eye, Garnet, Red Jasper or Ruby
- Bathe in the red colour in your clothing, decor, art, etc.

# Part II

These questions are connected to your Orange Spleen chakra power.

The Spleen chakra is your sensing power station, connecting you to your feeling sensitivities. It is the center that allows you to live consciously, in the "now." The spleen center is also the link to your enthusiasm, happiness and joy—your inner-child.

## Issues to review are:

1. Are you emotionally stable or do your emotions go from one extreme to another?
2. Do you try to hide or control your feelings?
3. Is your inner child still alive, enthusiastic and uninhibited?
4. Can you think outside of the box or is your creative perception restricted?
5. Are your sexual relationships mutual and respectful, and can you be totally comfortable with your partner with no limitations such as frigidity or impotence?
6. Do you feel disconnected from reality and do you have a difficult living in the present moment?

## Ways to bring in the ORANGE energy and boost your Spleen chakra power are:

- Hot aromatic baths, water aerobics, deep tissue massage, emotional movies, cooking classes., embracing sensation (such as different food tastes)
- Eat orange foods and consume orange drinks
- Use aromatherapy oils such as melissa, orange, mandarin, neroli, tangerine
- Music with a bounce or that flows (running water, thunderstorms, etc.), harp
- Wear or carry an orange gemstone or copper piece., orange stones would be Coral or Carnelian
- Bathe in the orange colour in your clothing, colour bath™, decor, art, etc.

# Part III

These questions are connected to your Yellow Solar Plexus chakra power.

The Yellow chakra is your mental awareness, which connects you to your mind power. It is the center that governs your ability to learn and comprehend. The solar plexus center is known to govern your ego and your will power. It is the sun center that emits optimism and confidence.

## Issues to review are:

1. Are you too flexible and are your focus and concentration abilities poor?
2. Do you lack confidence that you are overly concerned with what other people think?
3. Are your thoughts clouded so that you have a difficult time making decisions?
4. Do you take on too much responsibility because you think you know best?

5. Are you a perfectionist and prefer to do things yourself?
6. Are you afraid to be alone?

## Ways to bring in the YELLOW energy and boost your Solar Plexus chakra power are:

- Taking classes, reading informative books, doing mind puzzles, developing one's photographic memory,sunshine, detoxification programs.
- Eat yellow foods and consume yellow beverages.
- Use aromatherapy oils such as rosemary, lemon, grapefruit, bergamot
- Music that is mentally stimulating such as chimes, reed and horn instruments.
- Wear or carry a yellow gemstone or something gold. Yellow stones would be Citrine, Amber, Topaz.
- Bathe in the yellow colour in your clothing, , decor, art, etc.

# Part IV

These questions are connected to your Green Heart chakra power.

The Green chakra is your heart power station, connecting you to your emotions. It is the center that allows you to love and give unconditionally. The heart center governs your relationships. It is the energy center that integrates one's physical reality to one's spiritual connection.

## Issues to review are:

1. Do you accept yourself for who you are or do you lack self-love?
2. Do you feel that you are not worthy of living life fully or do you feel stifled (feel a lack of freedom in your life)?
3. Are you indecisive because you can't make up your mind?
4. Do you have a hard time saying "no" to people?

5. Do you have a fear of being rejected or abandoned?
6. Are you envious and jealous of what other people have?

## Ways to bring in the GREEN energy and boost your Heart chakra power are:

- Nature hikes, spending time with family or friends, surrounding yourself with plants, gardening, taking self-love courses, reading romantic novels or watching romantic movies, candlelight dinners
- Eat green foods and consume green drinks
- Use aromatherapy oils such as Eucalyptus, Pine, Tea Tree, Spearmint, Cedarwood
- Music that has the sounds of nature
- Wear or carry a green gemstone, Green stones would be Aventurine, Emerald, Jade, Malachite, Peridot
- Bathe in the green colour in your clothing, decor, art, etc.

# Part V

These questions are connected to your Blue Throat chakra power.

The Blue chakra is your communication power station. It is the center that handles incoming and outgoing messages. It is through this center that we voice our opinions and our truths.

## Issues to review are:

1. Are you able to express yourself and your beliefs (voice your inner truth)?
2. Do you have the ability to trust others without doubt?
3. Do you have good organization and planning skills?
4. Are you able to free yourself of old family values, beliefs and commitments especially regarding their relationship to responsibility?
5. Are you concerned with financial security and having nice possessions?

6. Are you shy and have difficulty communicating yourself or are you too talkative?

## Ways to bring in the BLUE energy and boost your throat chakra power are:

- Singing (in the shower) and toning., poetry, stamp or art collecting, meaningful conversations, taking self-development courses, attending church or spiritual functions. Journaling, neck and shoulder rolls
- Eat blue foods and consume blue beverages
- Use aromatherapy oils such as Geranium, Chamomile, Peppermint, Mint, Cypress
- Music that is repetitive, such as echoes or sounds of ocean waves.
- Wear or carry a blue gemstone,blue stones would be Sodalite, Lapis Lazuli, Sapphire, Blue Agate
- Bathe in the blue colour in your clothing, decor, art, etc.

# Part VI

These questions are connected to your Indigo Brow chakra power.

The Indigo chakra is your intuitive intelligence. It is the center that taps into the universal consciousness. Through the third-eye you can see things from a psychic potential.

## Issues to review are:

1. Do you trust your intuition and insights?
2. Are you able to develop your psychic and intuitive abilities?
3. Can you release your fears and anxieties or do you hang on to negative thoughts?
4. Are you able to balance your imagination and fantasy realm with reality?

5. Do you tend to feel lonely or are you often depressed?

6. Are you unable to give yourself credit because you lack self-pride?

## Ways to bring in the INDIGO energy and boost your Brow chakra power are:

- Star gazing, eye rolls, meditation developing one's intuition and psychic abilities
- Eat indigo foods and consume indigo drinks
- Use aromatherapy oils such as Patchouli, Frankincense, Myrrh
- Music such as Mozart or Bach. Chanting (OM).
- Wear or carry an indigo gemstone or silver jewllery. Indigo stones are Amethyst, Tourmaline, Tanzanite
- Bathe in the indigo colour in your clothing, decor, art, etc.

# Part VII

These questions are connected to your Violet Crown chakra power.

The Violet chakra is your spiritual connection. This chakra links you to the cosmos so you can reach your higher potential. It is the energy of knowingness and enlightenment.

## Issues to review are:

1. Are you dedicated to the Divine consciousness?

2. Do you trust the universe and your spiritual reality?

3. Are you able to equally balance your spirituality with your ability to stay grounded?

4. Do you allow the universal energy to flow through you so that you have an unlimited creative energy source?

5. Are you able to integrate you intuitive energy with your intellect—your feminine energy with your masculine energy?

6. Do you lack faith because you prefer to believe in your own abilities?

## Ways to bring in the VIOLET energy and boost your Crown chakra power are:

- Focusing on dreams and writing down one's visions and inventions, quiet contemplation, meditation and yoga, listening to guided meditation tapes, taking spiritual courses
- Eat violet foods and consume violet beverages
- Use aromatherapy oils such as Lavender, Jasmine, Magnolia
- Silence is the violet inspiration's music, Crystal Bowls
- Wear or carry a violet gemstone. Violet stones would be Quartz Crystal, Diamond
- Bathe in the violet colour in your clothing, decor, art, etc.

# Chapter 12

# Example of a Dysfunctional Chakra System

The root, spleen, throat and brow centers are illustrating energy deficiencies (under-activity); whereas the solar plexus and crown chakra centers are over-active. In this case the chakra system indicates that the individual has little "red" fire to push the "chi" energy through their system. Lack of a healthy root driving force suggests that this person is unable to accomplish their goals or lacks a supportive relationship. A feeling of tiredness would validate this on a physical level.

Basically this person's chakra system is already in trouble. However, since this individual's solar plexus and crown centers are their main

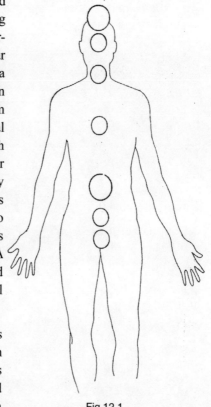

Fig.12.1

power stations, they could be accomplishing some tasks as their mental and visionary energies are able to achieve their goals. But on a foundation level they are not very strong and therefore may eventually burn out so that other root or chakra imbalances prevail.

# Chapter 13

# Chakra Theory Combined to Homeopathic Treatment

Let me give a simple example then of elemental diagnosis. A client came to me who had recurrent serious kidney infections that were getting progressively worse. She was thin, almost wasting away and with no energy. She said that she felt that she was slowly dying .

In taking her case I noted that she had a medical history of eczema, asthma, and IBS. All of these had previously been successfully 'treated' homoeopathically in the past. Emotionally she was very prone to anxiety and fear, and had a lot of basic survival issues (always a sense of lack; money worries; a sense of not really belonging or being welcome anywhere).

Each element is responsible for the building and maintenance of specific organs and systems in the body. So where as to find the right homeopathic remedy with a symptom like eczema we need to know the concomitants, location, aetiology, modalities etc, etc, to do an elemental analysis we simply need to know where the symptom is.

## To summarise it:

| Ether | *The whole body especially throat, thyroid and joints. All emotions, grief* |
|-------|------|
| Air | *Skin, kidneys, intestines, lungs, nerves and heart. Anxiety. Thin body-type* |
| Fire | *Brain, liver, stomach, pancreas, gall bladder, heart. Anger and power issues. Medium or athletic body-type* |

| Water | *Reproductive organs, breasts, lungs, kidneys, lymph, heart. Addictions, sexual issues, guilt. Rounded or fleshy body-type* |
|-------|---------|
| Earth | *Skeletal structure, intestines, adrenals. Fear, survival issues. Solid body-type* |

Arranging the client's symptoms under the elements gives us:

| Ether | *Anxiety.* |
|-------|---------|
| Air | *Kidneys, skin (eczema), lungs (asthma), intestines (IBS). Anxiety. Body-type* |
| Fire | *None* |
| Water | *Lungs (asthma)* |
| Earth | *Intestines (IBS). Fear, survival issues* |

We then need to assess what is happening overall with her elements. A common mistake here is to think that because an element has either no or few symptoms it must be lacking. Remember that what we have written down here are symptoms. An element with no symptoms is fine! What she did have is a clear underlying imbalance of the air element. Almost by definition it is also common for airy people to lack earth (the two elements are in many ways opposites). She clearly exhibited a lack of earth; her lack of grounding came across clearly in when you met her, and matches her symptoms. In fact, peoples symptoms nearly always match their elemental imbalance, since it is the elemental imbalance that creates much of the symptoms. The physical body is built according to the elemental blueprint. This is to the extent that once you learn to read the body you could predict most of what a client's symptoms are.

Coming back to the case example a simple elemental analysis is that the client is excessively airy and lacks earth. This fundamental underlying imbalance had never been directly treated. The homeopathic treatment, even though some of it had been what we would call constitutional treatment, had in fact only been palliating in acute episodes. She had had all the indicated homeopathic remedies. Homeopathy had successfully treated the acutes, but the underlying imbalance had continued to develop and was now potentially life threatening.

*So how can we treat this case energetically?* To explain this I need to outline a further piece of the energy model. This is best illustrated by looking at the creation of the Universe. Physicist currently believe that the Universe was created by the explosion of a singularity (the so called Big Bang theory). Initially the movement away from the center of explosion consisted of waves of pure energy. As these waves imperceptibly slowed down, they organised themselves into individual photons (literally little packages of light). As these photons slowed down they split forming particles with mass and charge (mostly protons and electrons). The protons and electrons then paired up, forming hydrogen gas. The gas collected into individual stars which eventually exploded, throwing out quantities of all the other chemical elements. These chemical elements then start to combine, creating entirely new substances. With carbon these new molecules can be increasingly complex and form the building blocks of life itself. We are, literally, made of stardust, which itself is slowed-down light.

So what is happening here is as energy moves from fast to slow we see the emergence of physical matter and increasing complexity: the movement from singularity to diversity. Conversely if we take some complex matter and speed it up again (i.e. add energy to it) the complexities start to break down and in the end we are left with uniformity. There is a spectrum from fast-vibration (singularity, uniform, non-material) through to slow-vibration (diverse, complex, physical).

In the energy model this process is understood to extend further back than what we can physically observe – into the realm of subtle energy. In other words, there are further realms before energy manifests in the physical universe. Modern physics has just recently caught up with this (for instance some physicists now believe that the singularity that created the Universe was itself created by the collision of two 'membranes' in the eleventh dimension).

All this gives us a practical map for understanding remedies. There is a lot of theory we could go into here but for the purposes of this introduction we'll just look at three simple categories:

1. **Fast-vibration remedies.** These are remedies made from pure energy. They include colour remedies and sound remedies. Also in this category we can put gem elixirs and flower remedies given that they are made with the etheric imprint of the substance (rather than a tincture of the physical substance itself).

2. **Mid-vibration remedies.** These are remedies prepared from physical substances which are then potentised to enhance their vibrational rate. This of course includes most homeopathic remedies, and spagiric tinctures.

3. **Slow-vibration remedies.** These are remedies prepared from physical substances without vibrational enhancement. This group includes herbs, nutritional supplements and indeed allopathic drugs.

As I said the energy model provides us with much more detailed mapping than this. But this will suffice for the purposes of the case example.

One of the things having and energy model gives us is an understanding of how different therapeutic interventions fit together. For instance a practitioner may prescribe a combination of acupuncture, herbs, dietary measures and meditation practice, all based on the underlying energy diagnosis. Similarly an ayurvedic practitioner may prescribe dietary advice, herbs, yoga and even homeopathic remedies, again based on the energetic diagnosis. If we look again at the case example we can see that her previous treatments have all been at the mid-vibrational level. When treatment is only palliating or only partially successful what the energy model shows is that we may need to come in at a different vibrational level. With my client what she was lacking was earth – slow vibration. This is why the traditional treatment had only been palliating. My first prescription for her was to build her up at this fundamental, earthy level. And so, along with the homeopathic prescription, I suggested e 'building diet'(rather than a cleansing diet, which would have finished her off!). This consisted of lots of cooked warm building foods. I also suggested supplements, particularly lots of minerals and herbs (what she needed was herbs that are building, not cleansing).

"But this isn't homeopathy" some people will now be crying. If so, I can only suggest you go back to the Organon and just look at just how many times Hahnemann states the need for dietary treatment. In fact he includes environmental factors (including faulty nutrition) as being one of the three possible causes of chronic disease (aphorism #77), the other two being miasm (#78) and drug induced (#74). His approach to diet is, of course, coloured by the times and location he wrote in, and so has a western naturopathic slant to it. I have no doubt that in another time or culture, his dietary advice would have been different. The fact is though that he saw attention to diet as important. He does of course advocate not using herbs with strong medicinal action whilst taking homeopathic remedies. Personally I believe it would be perfectly possible to do one thing at a time, prescribing the herbs and dietary changes first and then the homeopathic treatment.

Other people may object to using herbs at all. However there is a great and long tradition of using mother tinctures in homeopathy. What the energy model gives us is a framework to do this in an intelligent, highly effective and integrated manner.

In any case what is really important here, the only thing that is really important here, is the patient's health. What happened was she came back a month later saying that she felt better than she had done in years. My next prescription was to continue the diet, nutritional and herbal support, and to introduce some tissue salts (Silica, Calc Phos. and Kali Phos.), to continue to build at an earthy level.

The other area which she had not been treated in was fast vibration remedies. There are two major things we can do here. The first is to directly work with the underlying energy imbalance. The five elements (ether, air, fire, water, earth) originate from five centers in the body – the five lower chakras. The chakras resonate with colour frequencies. The traditional correspondences are:

- Crown – Violet
- Brow – Indigo
- Throat – Blue/Turquoise – Ether
- Heart – Green - Air
- Solar Plexus – Yellow - Fire
- Sacral – Orange - Water
- Base – Red - Earth

This is based on the understanding that as the chakras represent a spectrum of energy moving from fast to slow, in seven divisions, so there will be a harmonic resonance the colour spectrum, which also represents a movement from fast to slow in seven divisions. These correspondences seem to be the most widely used, appearing in several different cultures and periods of time. Occasionally one comes across other systems of colour-chakra correspondences.

One thing that is important to note here is that the remedies used to treat the underlying elemental/chakra imbalance will need usually need persistent treatment (similar, say, to treating a miasm). Exactly how long for is impossible to say, in the same way that we can not really say how long it takes to treat a miasm; it depends on the client. An individual's fundamental elemental imbalance is only very rarely going to change forever with a single dose of a remedy.

Something that can really help here in treating the element imbalance is the second thing we can do at the fast vibrational level – that is to address the reasons why the client's elements have become imbalanced in the first place. With respect to my client, she had been the unplanned and unwanted child of emotionally abusive parents. Essentially she had received the message from childhood that it was not safe to be here. She became ungrounded as a response. Core beliefs such as these respond very well to treatment with well-chosen flower essences and gem elixirs, since these remedies focus primarily on thoughts and emotions. There are many sets of flower remedies available now. It is simply a question of choosing a set, or sets, that you feel drawn to. Spread through the different sets there are many different flower remedies that would have been appropriate for my client. What I wish to get across here in not about which actual flower essences or gem elixirs I used. Rather I wish to convey the idea (and usefulness) of using such essences to deal with core beliefs that are a maintaining cause in disease.

Along the way, she still needed traditional homeopathic remedies too. The difference being that she felt that these now held far better than they had done in the past. She began to gain healthy weight and became much more grounded and less fearful. During this process she learnt a lot about herself. Particularly she became aware of how being airy and ungrounded was her habitual response to stress, about the ways in which she kept herself airy, and about what being ungrounded was costing her. After a year of treatment she left, saying that she felt better than she ever had done in her life.

So, I believe the best way to integrate the chakra system in homeopathic treatment is to work individually with the patient during consultation to cleanse and balance the 'dis-eased' chakra center.

The best way to do it is to guide the patient during consultation with specific exercises so that he or she will be able to do them at home, according to their time and their spaces.

# Chapter 14

# Auras, Chakras and Energy Fields: Cleansing and Activating your Energy Systems

## Why Look After Our Energy Systems

Our energy systems are alive and intelligent. They know exactly what they need for perfect health and vibrant energy. When our energy systems are disrupted, blocked, slowed down, or damaged, messages are sent to the conscious level that something is wrong and that we need to address imbalances, blockages and damage. We are trained to look at the physical body and address its needs rather than look at our energetic systems to provide them what they need for perfect health. Our energy systems are conscious energy and this energy is connected with all energies in the Universe. Our energy systems act as a connection between the physical world and the metaphysical or spiritual world. When we look after our energy systems we look after our deepest and most profound needs, including the physical, emotional intellectual and spiritual.

# About Auras, Chakras, Meridians

## Auras:

An aura is an energy field that surrounds, penetrates and extends out beyond the physical body, that is electromagnetic, electric and magnetic and is made up of varying types of live and intelligent vibrations or frequencies. An aura surrounds not only every living thing including humans, animals and plants, but also every inanimate thing such as rocks, all objects made by man, and the earth, sun, moon, and all planets in our Universe. The human aura has layers of physical, emotional, mental and spiritual elements.

Auras contain all the primary colours of the rainbow at any given time and change colour depending on the emotion an individual is experiencing. Our auras are made up of may colours and many shades of colours that are constantly changing. This reflects the constant change in our thoughts and emotions.

Happy and loving thoughts expand your aura while sad or angry thoughts contract your aura. Aura sizes adjust depending on the density of the population where you live.

## Chakras:

Chakras are spinning wheels of electric energy of different colours that perform many functions connecting our energy fields, bodies and the broader Cosmic Energy Field. Chakras are directly connected to and govern the endocrine system that in turn regulates the aging process.

The chakras are linking mechanisms between the auric field and the meridian system within the physical body and different levels of the auric fields and cosmic forces. They affect the flow of energy into the physical body. They absorb primary energy from the atmosphere (called chi, prana, orgone) and send it along energy channels. Chakras are energy transformers.

Our bodies contain seven major chakras or energy centers and 122 minor chakras. The major chakras are located at the base of the spine (Root Chakra), at the navel (Sacral Chakra), in the solar plexus (Solar Plexus Chakra), within your heart (Heart Chakra), within the throat (Throat Chakra), at the centers of your forehead (Brow or Third Eye Chakra), and at the top of your head (Crown Chakra). These chakras are linked together.

## The Entire Energy System - Within, Around and Penetrating Us:

Our energy systems surrounds us, are inside of us, and penetrates us completely. This includes the light body, which extends beyond our auras and I believe is the very essence of us that goes on forever, our auras that surround us and penetrate our physical bodies, the meridian system, a system of energy channels within us through which all energy moves throughout our body, as well as the chakras, the energy transformers changing and processing live giving prana within us. The issues and care which I describe for auras and chakras, applies to the entire energetic system within, around, and penetrating us.

## Potential Aura, Chakra and Meridian System Issues

There are many issues that can affect the functioning of our auras, chakras, and meridian systems leading to a variety of health problems. The following are a number of key potential issues.

(i)    Blockages can be caused by any of the following: emotions that have not been felt and released; negative thought forms from others; psychic attack energy or negative energy from energetic spells; entities or spirits lodged in our auras or chakras; chemical, metal and atomic toxins; other types of poisons or toxins; past life memories or experiences.

(ii)    Distorted auras and chakras can be caused by any of the issues identified under blockages.

(iii) Holes in the auras can be caused by any of the issues identified under blockages.

(iv) Lack of synchronization between the auras, chakras, and meridian system can create serious difficulty. Physical issues, emotional issues, intellectual imbalances or spiritual issues can create imbalances in various parts of the auras, chakras and meridian system. These imbalances affect the specific aura or chakra that in turn affects other parts of the energetic system. Nature always tries to achieve perfect balance and these imbalances create a real disharmony in our energetic systems. This can create unbalanced thinking, feeling and behaviour.

(v) Negative connections and rays can become attached to our auras. These are a result of negative emotions, drug and alcohol use, psychic attacks or spells, other intelligent being in the Cosmic World, environmental pollution, lack of nature i.e. trees, plants and flowing water. Negativity in thought and behaviour in individuals, communities, draws negative forces to us from the broader Universe. These connections, rays and energies can have a real negative effect on our vitality and energy.

(vi) Energetic and chemical markings can be left by other dimensional beings in our auras and brains so that these energetic beings can find and track us. Constant interference by other dimensional beings can seriously affect our vitality and health.

(vii) Negative energy programs can be sent into an individual by other human beings. These programs establish connections so that ongoing negative energy can be run into an individual. This can have a serious effect on our entire energy system and inner vitality.

(viii) Negative energy can easily flip from one individual's aura into your aura. Energy is alive, moves around, and you can eventually become quite affected by the negative energy of those around you, in your homes, offices or stores.

(ix) Imbalances cab be created by earth energies especially the intersecting points of the Hartman and Curry grids and underground running water.

(x) Underactive or overactive chakras can create a variety of issues. Underactive chakras can translate into fatigue, lethargy, weight problems, just a slow attitude towards life or a lack of zest for living. Overactive chakras create other types of problems including hyperactivity, panic attacks, emotional imbalances, and many types of health issues in the physical body.

# Major Effects of Negative Energies

There can be so many different effects from energetic issues. The following is a limited listing of certain major potential effects.

(i) Fatigue

(ii) Lacking vitality or a zest for life

(iii) Negative or distorted thinking

(iv) Negative, unbalanced or distorted emotions

(v) Negative, unbalanced or distorted behaviour

(vi) Feeling disconnected from other human beings

(vii) Feeling disconnected from the Creator or whatever we choose to call our Higher Power

(viii) Feeling disconnected from nature

(ix) Panic attacks that can be caused by a vulnerability caused by holes in our auras

(x) A compromised energy system leads to many types of physical illnesses.

## Identifying the Overall Status of Your Energy System

There are many different ways to identify the health status of your energy systems but an experienced dowser or intuitive can help you identify the strengths and weaknesses of the many parts of your energy system.

## Cleansing and Activating Auras, Chakras and Energy Systems

Since our auras, chakras, and meridian systems are affected by things physical, intellectual, emotional, and spiritual, the answer to looking after our energetic aspects falls under these same heading. The following are summaries of the physical, intellectual, emotional and spiritual ways to effect clearing, rebalancing, activating and healing of your energy systems and all aspects are interconnected and all aspects are required for healthy and vibrant living.

**Smudging with white sage** clears out certain types of negative energy blockages in your auras, chakras as well as your home. All you need to do is seal your room closing windows and doors, burn some white sage so that the smoke fills your room, and remain in that room and many negative energies will dissolve, within you and your home. Or just burn a few leaves moving the smoke through your auras and negative energies will dissolve.

**Auric brushing** or having someone run their hands down your aura from top to bottom can help release blockages in your auras. **Crystals and gems** can be used to clear out blockages in your auras but one needs to be experienced to do this type of clearing and often crystals and gems are too strong and can create serious damage in the auras and chakras rather than be part of the healing process.

A **healthy diet, clean and vibrant water,** and lots of **sleep and relaxation** are essential to having healthy energetic systems. High ongoing stress creates serious damage in auras and chakras as well as the physical body.

**Physical exercise** and certain types of **breatheing exercises** are an important element of a healthy energetic system. I highly recommend the book "Science of Breathe" by Yogi Ramacharaka that describes a series of breathing exercises for vibrant health. All types of **physical exercise** help to activate the chakras. One set of exercises that are outstanding for activating the chakras and auras are called the **Five Tibetan Rites**. I have written an article which contains photos of this exercise program that is so outstanding (www.mkprojects.com) but I strongly urge you to buy the book "Ancient Secret of the Fountain of Youth - Book 2" by Peter Kelder.

Cannot stress enough the healing process that can occur through the Five Tibetan Rites exercise program. This program activates underactive chakras and can be important in any health issues you might have, including weight difficulties.

**Connecting with nature** has a profound effect on your energy systems. There are many ways to use nature such as connecting with trees; communicating with all types of nature; using vibrational essences such as Choming Essences which are made from nature to effect healing at all levels; using water for healing of energy systems; being with nature and allowing the vibration of nature to bring healing into your energy system.

**Healing with colour** is powerful. Different colours have different vibrations that affect different elements of a person. E.g. green is a colour that affects healing and calmness so if you want to focus on staying calm and supporting your healing, wear the colour green, do some pore breathing with the colour green, visualize that you are breathing in the colour green, or decorate your room with the colour green. If you want to feel energized, do the same with the colour red.

**Sound and music can be used** to heal the energy system. Sound can activate the chakras. There are different types of music being produced today that can activate chakras, which in turn activate the entire endocrine system.

**Intellectual stimulation and intellectual pursuits** are critical elements required for healthy energy systems. The mind rests in the mental aura and this level of the aura needs to be stimulated or it will slow down, accelerating the aging process. We need to be learning, interested, and passionate about something at all times in our lives.

It is only when we **spend time alone** that we can deeply communicate with our Higher Power, internalize the experiences of the day, get in touch with our thoughts and feelings, and ground ourselves so that we are truly with ourselves and our lives in that moment. You can go though life only partially experiencing what is actually happening to you, fairly unconscious to the experiences of the moment.

**Loving yourself and being able to give and receive love from family, friends and community** are important. When we feel love we release certain chemicals in our body and when we are angry we release a different set of chemicals. We have been made to achieve a certain balance and an imbalance in these types of emotions affects the vibrancy of our energy systems.

**Owning your emotions and being able to express your emotions** to others is fundamental to having a healthy energy system. Emotions not felt or expressed remain lodged in our physical and energetic bodies creating blockages, distorting our chakras, and creating holes in our auras. Repressed and unfelt emotions make us ill in the long-term. It's important to learn how to release emotions lodged within to release blockages and allow our chakras to function harmoniously and actively.

**Creativity in your life** is an vital element of a healthy energy system. Creativity is not necessarily painting or sculpting, but it can include these activities. It can also be cooking, gardening, needlework, studying, hiking, or many other different types of activities.

**Past lives** can play a major role in the health of our energy systems. Valerie Hunt in her book "The Infinite Mind" describes the effects of past lives in great detail. You can touch one of your past lives through meditation either alone or with an energy therapist. Past lives lodged in your auras can provide you with deep insight into your soul purpose or core issue for this life.

**Spiritual integrity** in all aspects of our lives is necessary for healthy and vibrant health. Values can become quite confused today. People can love their children and spouse, cheat at the office, are ruthless in business, help in their community, and be kind and generous with their aging parents. A lack of spiritual integrity in any aspect of life will seriously affect your energy system.

**Prayer and meditation** are central to the achievement of healthy energy systems. Prayer connects us with our Higher Power bringing emotional balance and stability. The power of prayer can be quite amazing. Meditation helps us quiet our busy minds so that we can become open to listening, being, and hearing from Universal Powers. These practices energize and heal our energy systems.

Integrating many of the above elements requires love of self, time and tenacity. I usually suggest to my clients that they begin with a few, and then continue to layer additional elements when they feel ready to do so.

# Chapter 15

# Diagnosis and Treatment

Specific methods of healing are unlimited as they are subtle and intricate. The dear reader should know that the following is only a coarse and rough outline of energy diagnosis and healing techniques. Left and right, front and back, top and bottom are easy ways to structure the diagnostic healing "search", and it can be done through visual examination, palpation, making passes with the hands to feel the qualities and densities of the energy, and/or analysis of the air flow through the nostrils. The front, bottom, and left sides of the body (along with the right brain crossing over at the third eye) is associated with the ida or chandra nadis while the back, top, and right side of the body (along with the left brain again crossing over at the third eye) is associated with the pingala or surya nadis.

For example if someone is overly contracted or collapsed forward being bent over to the front we may surmise that the surya nadi (pingala) is over active or the chandra nadis or ida is depleted or under active, because the pingala nadis (male energy not only is associated with the right side of the body and left brain (male) but also the back energy (rising up the back), while the ida is associated with the left side of the body, the right brain (crossing over at the third eye) and the energy running up the front of the body (female). In this as a simple experiment we might suggest the emphasis of backbends as a simple remedial measure. Most "illnesses" can be analyzed by simply analyzing the energy patterns, blockages, stagnations, depletion, flow, or their lack of flow and then treated to re-establish homeostasis.

Often a collapsed body which appears overly passive, yin, soft, yielding, hyper-parasympathetic tone, heightened afferent nervous function, ida dominant, over active afferent nerves, or right brain dominant function associated with the female will appear to be the opposite of a body which is stiff, rigid, armored, overly contracted, hard, yang, or other wise associated with hyper-sympathetic tone, over active efferent nerves, pingala, or male associated functions. These are two extreme energetic ways of viewing the possibilities, but we will suggest that even what appears as a collapse is often do to an energy dam, a contraction and folding inward as protection around an old pain, trauma, unresolved conflict inhibition, weakness, feeling of vulnerability, fear, grief, etc. with the obvious exception of situations that are drug induced or the result of over stretched ligaments.

The many possible situations will speak to us very clearly and our own activated energy body will go directly to the balanced (correct) mode of intervention. In other situations the causal obstruction may mirror a similar obstruction that is imbedded or brings up a resonant blockage in our own mental/emotional (manomaya kosha) , energy (pranamaya kosha), or belief system (jnanamaya kosha) bodies so that we may either be forced to do healing on ourselves or otherwise be stumped.

Similarly we may find often the energetic problem is a symptom reflecting past conditioning, a stubbornly held core belief system, armoring and contraction around a past trauma, an imbedded fear, guilt, past negative karma or habits -- animosity, anger, grudges, greed, compensatory desires, complexes glued together in anger, and many other similar energetic propensities that have components other than the "simply" the physical. All these holistic relationships and more can be accessed and positively influenced through "energy work", but the therapist must embrace the holistic framework wherein there is no isolation/separation between the body/mind, belief systems, life styles, thoughts, and emotions from that of the physical symptoms. Here the therapist must be firmly grounded, centered, and balanced in their own core/heart energy and thus able to accept the patients pain, fear, and other such elements of disease without themselves being disturbed or negatively influenced -- in order for the therapist to be fully present and effective and creatively and joyfully work responsibly.

Classically; the chakras can exist in :

1. A state of deficiency (depletion) which is often cool or blue.

2. Distortion, congestion, and stress (where the flow is blocked above or below it) which is sometimes mistaken as being diagnosed as "over active". This can also appear often as being represented as being hot or red; or

3. In a state of healthy and synchronized interactive flow.

In other words disease may manifest in energy terms as an imbalance, a depletion, or a congestion while "treatment" is always aimed at re-balancing and removing stasis to the "natural and healthy" flow of energy which includes purifying/opening the congested channels and/or centers. Here we can cool the hot and over active (overly rajasic) and heat the overly cold and sluggish (tamasic) if we chose to use the Ayurvedic breakdown of the three gunas which are composed of rajas (hot and stimulating), satva (balanced and pure), and tamas (slow and cool). There of course exist equal richness in the Chinese energetic system (yin/yang, cool/hot, wet/dry, etc.). Such approaches include techniques of energizing/stimulating on one hand or soothing/calming/cooling on the other while re-establishing balance and harmony – re-activating the innate dormant evolutionary/ creative circuitry.

Most schools emphasize first purification of the area, then removal of congestion (sweeping) and lastly then energizing or balancing the area. Indeed this will avoid some untoward effects if one were start first energizing without clearing the obstructions to the flow, but in some cases where the energy is already critically depleted and the patient is very weak and cold, energization at first may be best.

*The overall description of our approach can be simplified even further by stating that the process can be reduced to the idea of purification of the channels and pathways because purification will at the same time remove obstruction of flow in the area where it is blocked (thus facilitating removal of congestion) and at the same time the energy is now able to flow to energize the areas that may have been depleted (due to the blockage/obstruction). A careful reading will show that purification not only relieves congestion and restores depletion, but also restores balance and homeostasis simply because the energy is now flowing unobstructed being self regulated by the natural intelligence inherent in the healthy organism. This is not unlike some shamanistic techniques which use a form of drawing out of an evil spirit or exorcism in order to effect the overall "cure".*

1) It is essential first to take on the responsibility of understanding and healing ourselves and then we are able to heal others, i.e., to surrender to the innate and indigenous healing powers and intelligence within). Many times this can happen simultaneously, but it must always include taking care of your own energy system and never approaching pranic healing as a sacrifice, barter, or transfer of your personal energy (but rather it is always more valuable to stay in tune always with the transpersonal universal life energy acting from this central intelligent core as much as possible). One must realize that this is the same evolutionary energy that is inside of all of life and creation (it is not an exclusive or personal endogenous ability, but rather transpersonal as a result of millions of years of co-creative/co-evolutionary interdependent dynamic inter-relationships).

2) It helps to ask for help from some "outside" force that you have a balancing affinity with such as a specific helper from the angel, deva, plant or animal spirit world, archetypal world of gods and goddesses, the universe (such as the sun or stars, nature/creation/creator in general, or at the very least your highest self). Be sure to thank these helpers (usually silently) at the end and ascribe any "miracles" to them (rather than the lower self or ego). This will save us trouble falling back into duality and increase our abilities to align with infinite power and wisdom in the long run. We are all in this together even though our present culture or peers will not acknowledge that "fact".

There exist many techniques in psychic healing that are similar while many practitioners are interdisciplinary and eclectic incorporating more than one of these techniques. Given the two basic techniques above, the following specific techniques may or not be suitable for everyone.

3) Next we can concentrate our awareness on our own back body (light body) grounding the tailbone deep into the earth and at the same time extending the line of energy through the crown to the highest point (brahmabindu at the brahmarandhra) connecting up with the formless Seed/Source above and the Abundant Mother below. Intend that love be embodied and healing be done now. Wash out the hands and cleanse your own system. Activate internal flow especially through (in and out) from the feet and hands. Focusing upon your own light body, sensitize and charge your hands. Get in touch with the feet, chakras, belly, and breathe in relationship with the back body. Go deep inside for this conscious connection. In this regard even the slightest amount of bodhicitta helps tremendously in transforming any possible negative conditions.

4) Scan the person's aura asking questions with your hand not mouth) such as is this hot or cold, thick or thin, red or blue, clockwise or counter-clockwise, congested and full versus depleted and desirous of energy, and so forth maintaining an inner dialogue of asking questions and allowing for answers. One method is to use the finger tips of one hand to receive prana and the center of the opposite palm to send it, but both can be used. The fingers can also be allowed to perform delicate actions and in Huna each finger is assigned a corresponding element quality. The hand can also sense vortexes and synchronize and re-tune the existing vortexes. Approach these subtle possibilities with loving attention and let the intelligence of the client guide you. As mentioned cleansing alone is often sufficient to allow for healing to occur because it opens flow from congested areas so that it can energize depleted areas and reestablish balance, but if you are good at concentration, very specific operations may be attempted

with the finger tips as long as you have a good diagnosis and a clear idea of what you are doing. For many this diagnosis stage can seem like an artificial imposition, an unnecessary limitation, get in the way, or slow things down so that they combine this step (four) with step five (below) as one process/movement.

5) After the energy diagnosis we can purify and open the systems that felt clogged and obstructed, energize the areas from the source of prana (use the sun if need be), and soothe, calm, and sweep out and clear any areas that still feel congested. Perform any specific operations or visualizations that you desire after entering more deeply. There exist an unlimited amount of possibilities here. For instance in some systems the hands are placed on two chakras of choice simultaneously. For example one hand may be placed over or on the sacrum (at the muladhara chakra) and the other hand over or on the back of the occiput (talu chakra) as in craniosacral and polarity therapy). In a similar approach the hands are placed over a chosen center/chakra (one hand in front of that center and the other hand in the back of the same center) simultaneously. For example in many Reiki moves and craniosacral therapies. In some forms of Jin Shin Do, fingers touch two or more acupuncture points simultaneously transferring, balancing, and harmonizing psychic energy flows. In another system the hands never really touch the physical body, etc. The point here is that after the awareness of the energy vibrations and pulses are attuned to through opening the nadis (energy channels/pathways) within ourselves then we are able to consciously direct the energy through intention. Cit means conscious awareness and prana means energy. Here we work with the cit-prana by becoming aware of the connection within of the energy as well as the energy of consciousness itself. Even without knowing the exact pathways consciously, just the subtle awareness and the intention are sufficient to allow the energy to move because the prana as the life force has an innate intelligence. After awhile we can apply the cit-prana at will, focusing on any area, both in ourselves and others. As our own eyes open, we open to the possibilities in the world and in others.

Many more detailed variations are possible and if so called to, many include working with the elements (water, air, fire, earth, and akasha (ether), the elementals (intelligent dynamic relationships and guardians formed around various natural phenomena), plants, totems, nature spirits, subtle form bodies, spirits, and the Great Spirit. Connecting up energy centers, balancing and harmonizing the previously restricted body/mind energy flows, opening up blockages, calming and cooling irritated or over loaded areas, stimulating previously strangulated and dormant centers, reprogramming negative emotional and mental habits, and similar approaches requires sensitivity – a requisite degree of waking up – of being open.

Humans have not perfected "healing" as a perfect science, but one can become more efficacious by matching the most efficacious modality to the right person. This then depends on the previous sections being developed by learning how to be present with "the other" and to listen openly and completely without judgment (listen and look from one's inner sense of knowing or innate intelligence), to have the courage and compassion to be with that person's pain and suffering. This requires the "healer" to be centerd, aligned, stabilized, and grounded in their own core energy being – it requires the self confidence, courage, inspiration, consciousness, compassion, and self empowerment that such integrated groundedness affords. This comes with openness, receptivity, loving intent, and **practice**. Healing, loving intent, and spirit leads.

6) Ending the session, make sure you exit slowly and **intend** that all things be placed where they belong. End up with stabilizing and grounding techniques while compacting the client's energy body (containing their energy within an aura of love and healing) while slowly withdrawing your "touch" and energy with a healing prayer for the benefit off all beings. Here we can seal the energy body, but always with the clear conscious intent to allow the good, healing, natural, and loving energies to be able to enter and the noxious elements to leave (being recycled back by mother

nature). For example carbon dioxide, human waste, pus, etc are food for the plants, bacteria, worms, etc. In turn animal and plant "waste" provide the basis for human food, energy, and air.

For example in Huna specifically, we are taught how to leave a drain for any noxious contamination to complete its removal over time, and/or how to empower temporary elemental allies to provide healing assistance for specific time periods when those elements can form a synergistic relationship. Man is ally to nature in his evolved modality. As such man is here to act as allies in healing and evolution with all of nature, just as nature is here to assist man. This natural healing relationship in the modern world has been mostly forgotten, but nonetheless this tragedy of dismemberment can be invoked – a host of allies are available should our heart allow.

It is a good idea to generate the bodhicitta (the aspiration for the complete enlightenment and end of confusion and suffering) at the crown chakra after withdrawing and let the client clearly know that you are finished with the session (verbally or symbolically), checking in with them that they are OK, and that they may take their time getting up. Finishing may vary considerably. One commonly effective method is to leave with the right hand on the client's third eye and the other hand on their heart or navel center checking in with them as to consciousness awareness (at the third eye) and joining that awareness to their heart or energy center (at the navel or heart) with a full body smile. Words are not always helpful or necessary. Check to ground yourself with mother earth and connect with father sky and again intend that this evolutionary and creative intelligent transpersonal loving energy that has created all of us become active and dominant in providing direction in our lives. Place confidence in this eternal omnipresent love, affirm, and surrender into it with infinite humility, gratitude, and joy in completion.

During a session there is a wealth of power and innate intelligence to draw from if only we are able to be present. Some healing approaches may include entering into verbal dialogue with the client while working; asking them what they want to accomplish; ask how they feel here or there, ask them to ascribe representative symbols to the feelings of disease or pain; have them recount a past experience that appears to be energetically related and provoke the catharsis of any associated emotions, feelings, and thoughts; ask them to participate in the process by breathing in a golden light into specific areas, and or moving energy in a specific region. A valuable skill is to always work in the present, knowing absolutely that it is the healer's ability to stay present that brings forth the insight and healing energy, that allows the healer to be effective, and as such the healing is always mutual and transpersonal. In this way the transpersonal healing infinite Source of the healing energy is invoked and amplified.

# Chapter 16

# Healer: Heal Yourself

A basic rule that "healers" often need to be reminded of is that there is an infinite amount of energy in the universe and that a yogic healer should NOT be transferring personal prana from self to the client, but rather is simply acting as an inter-mediator or transpersonal facilitator allowing the conscious source of the healers own life intelligence to communicate directly with the other person's conscious intelligent life energy and then after establishing contact allow the Source to facilitate change. In this way on a physical level we are asking the client's dna and intelligent energy patterns to communicate to the healer (agency) what the nature of the difficulty is and then have the healer communicate with Infinite Mind facilitating the necessary transfer of information and implementation through the physical structure of the hands.

If you are doing healing on others an important principle to implement is to not only ask permission, but inquire and evoke from the client the enthusiastic desire or intent to make a healing change in their own body/mind (whatever it takes) in order for healing to take place. Because without this receptive positive state as an energetic precursor, the effort may well be a waste of time. If the client has the attitude of "I don't want to change, just you (the practitioner) fix me so that I can go on with my life the same way", then the chances of an enduring success may be greatly diminished. When the client has a unified will toward becoming well, being healed, and coming into physical, emotional, and psychic health, then the process has less friction and becomes a process of mutual cooperative and education.

Change may be accompanied by both/or physical and mental catharsis (by catharsis one surrenders the obfuscations and noxious energy). Catharsis can be slow and sweet. Grieving and crying is often cathartic, however the expression of stored anger can sometimes re-traumatize, so when anger is touched upon it is titrated and allowed to come out while the facilitator holds the loving space -- stabilizes themselves in the healing process.

If the client has a need to talk (and it appears to be cathartic) then the facilitator may allow or even encourage it. If talk however seems to be resistive or escapist convince the client to go back into their breathe and/or give them a remedial visualization to do in order to help refocus the energy. If a catharsis occurs due to a painful past trauma or otherwise pain, fear, anger arise only a skilled facilitator strongly stabilized in their own core should continue to evoke this unless re-traumatization or over stimulation occur. Thus it is safest to pay attention to the client's energy, facial expressions, and breathing as gross signs of a deep unresolved disturbance perhaps triggering an over-stimulation reaction and if such a reaction is arising be able to know how to contain it, soothe the energy, balance it, and access a peaceful restorative mode when called for. These hyper-sensitive regions then can be returned to in future sessions and slowly titrated (brought into context without having the individual become overwhelmed by it).

# Chapter 17

# Grounding and Directing your Energy

## Grounding

1. Relax yourself, and breathe deeply. Release all tension.

2. Visualize your energy flowing freely from your Crown right down through all of your chakras to your Root Chakra.

3. Now, see your vital energy extend down, like a long tail from the base of your spine, through the Earth to its' molten Core.

4. Wrap your imaginary tail snugly around the earth's core. Send any negative energy in your body down through this tail to be neutralized by the Core.

5. Then, receive fresh, invigorating Earth energy up through this tail to your Root Chakra, then up to the rest of your body and chakras.

Our physical bodies are reflections of our use of energy. They reveal:

- Whether we are in balance
- Where we store energy blockages
- The strength and clarity of our flowing energy

## Power At Your Fingertips

Our hands are powerful transmitters of energy. They work similar to a magnet. Important chakras are located in the center of each palm.

### If you are Right handed :

Your Right Hand is positively charged and sends or gives energy. It emits the energy that "makes things happen".

Your Left hand is negatively charged, and receives energy. It emits the energy that "allows things to happen".

### If you are Left handed :

Your Left Hand is positively charged and sends or gives energy. It emits the energy that "makes things happen".

Your Right hand is negatively charged, and receives energy. It emits the energy that "allows things to happen".

Maintain a free - flowing passageway for your energy flow that extends from your Crown down along your spine to the palm of your hands and on further right through to the soles of your feet. In the middle of your soles, are two more important chakras that keep you grounded to the Earth's energy. Our longevity is related to our ability to integrate and synchronize our energy with the Earth's energy, and the energy of other people.

# Chapter 18

# More Exercises

## Opening & Closing the Chakra & Psychic Energy Centers

Firstly we will open the base or root chakra situated at the base of the spine and then work our way up opening all the main seven chakra. In this case we will see the base or root chakra as a small ball of Red coloured light and energy, visualise this chakra 2 to 4 inches in size. Now visualise this ball of Red energy growing in diameter and visualise it as though it is a flower that is still tightly in bud or as a lantern turned down low. As you open the chakra visualise it as the bud opening into a fully blooming flower or as a lantern being made brighter, allowing the energy center to open and expand.

This allows the spirit to sense and perceive beyond the normal senses and raises the spirits level of vibration and allows for the spirit to attune to use the sixth senses. As you open the chakra, draw in a deep breathe of this energy, breathe this colour deeply all the way into your lungs and let it fill your body and spirit. As you breathe it in you feel it's revitalising and healing energies, hold it in for a few seconds and then slowly breathe it all the way out, allowing all your daily worries and cares to flow out from you with it. This will help you to find the quieting and tranquillity of mind that is preferable for spiritual meditation of this kind, that is somewhat like a peaceful daydream like state of mind, where the subconscious can drift more freely free from the conscious minds control. Breathe this energy and colour in deeply 3 to 6 times.

## Repeat this exercise in the following chakras using the colours and locations described.

Next open the Sacral chakra in the same manner, situated 3 inches below the navel, this time visualising the chakra as a deep Orange ball of light and energy.

Next open the Solar-Plexus chakra in the same manner, situated within the Solar-Plexus, only this time visualising the chakra as a Yellow ball of light and energy, about twice the size of all the other chakra, as this is the largest and most powerful of all the chakra.

Next open the Heart chakra in the same manner, situated within the body over the heart, this time visualising the chakra over the heart as a Green ball of light and energy.

Next open the throat chakra in the same manner, situated within the voice box, this time visualising the chakra within the throat as an Indigo ball of light and energy.

Next open the brow chakra in the same manner, situated within the spiritual mind level with the brow, only this time visualising the chakra as a deep Purple ball of light and energy.

Lastly open the crown chakra in the same manner, situated 1 to 2 inches above the head, this time visualising the chakra as a Violet ball of light and energy.

# Closing the Chakra

It is important to close the chakra after any spiritual meditation or work, although the chakras never close completely. This is done quite quickly by reversing the opening process, visualize each of the chakra as the open flower and then closing each of the chakra back into the tightly closed bud or as a lantern being turned down low, or if you preferred to open the chakra like windows of the spirit and soul then close these windows. The reason for this is that if we do not close the chakra on occasion they can remain open and we can end up walking about being able to pick up spiritual and psychic impressions all the time and this can include negative experiences, therefore for beginners it is always best to close the chakra.

# Aura Chakra Cleansing

Chakra cleansing aims at helping to remove any negative energies and negatives that may have built up within your Chakra and Aura, this helps to remove any blockages from the chakra and aura that might of built up due to physical, mental or spiritual blockages or impurities and helps us to purify our chakra and aura. Firstly we will cleanse the seven main chakra then the rest of your chakras and finally your aura. You can do this as often as you like in a short meditation or however you prefer to do it.

Firstly see the Crown Chakra just above your head, visualize bright white light which contains all colours, coming into your crown chakra cleansing and revitalizing your chakra clearing any blockages and disharmonies until the chakra is brought back into balance. Allowing you to improve you energy flow, circulation and compassion to yourself and towards others and find the higher self.

Repeat this in your Brow Chakra, allowing you to be more intuitive and open up you spiritual sixth senses of the mind and helping you to open your third eye the psychic eye.

Repeat this in your Throat Chakra, allowing you to communicate more easily and to be truthful with love and wisdom.

Repeat this in your Heart Chakra. Allowing you to express your love and improve your relationships with others along with improving your circulation and energy flow.

Repeats this with your Solar Plexus Chakra, allowing you to receive more energy and to help you to open your main intuitive center and be more intuitive around others.

Repeat this with the Sacral Chakra, allowing you to have more intimacy at your digression with others.

Repeat this with the Base of Spine or Root Chakra. Allowing you to improve your energy flow and circulation.

Now breathe in the white light several times each time filling the whole of your body and mind with this light let the light go into your body down your arms and legs cleansing the rest of your Chakra as you breathe in, then as you expel your breathe let all negativities and impurities leave yourself, finally going through your feet into the ground, now expand the light several feet around yourself to cleans your aura getting ride of any impurities in the aura.

# Appendix A

## The Seven Rights

Each of the seven chakras has a basic right that, if infringed upon or not claimed or expressed, can provide problems in that chakra and thus, in that area of our life.

*1st Chakra. **The right to be here:*** Simply to exist, take care of ourselves, and have possessions.

*2nd Chakra. **The right to feel:*** To express and understand one's emotions, needs and wants.

*3rd Chakra. **The right to act:*** To be innovative and free.

*4th Chakra. **The right to love and be loved:*** Freedom from projected or received prejudice, low self-esteem, and violent conflict. Being the central chakra, if any of the other rights is harmed, the right to love may be harmed as well.

*5th Chakra. **The right to speak and hear truth:*** Transgressions include: not be listened to, family secrets, and not being spoken to honestly.

*6th Chakra. **The right to see:*** Transgressions include: being told our perception is inaccurate, having things deliberately hidden from us, and having the scope of ones vision denied.

*7th Chakra. **The right to know:*** The right to truth, accurate information, knowledge, and to simply know what's going on. This includes spiritual knowledge and the right to connect with and interpret the divine as one chooses.

# Appendix B

## The Demons/Tricksters of the Chakras

These are not fire spawned, brimstone bearing, biblical demons. They are symbolic and conceptual, as is most of what you have already read. We prefer to call them tricksters because although they do hinder the operations of the chakras, they generally do so to teach us something. The challenge of moving past a trickster helps the chakra in question learn how to better accomplish its "job."

*1st Chakra. Fear:* Comes when one's survival is threatened. May force energy into the upper chakras.

*2nd Chakra. Guilt:* Keeps us from reaching out, hindering emotional and sexual ties with others.

*3rd Chakra. Shame:* Hinders spontaneity, self-esteem, and personal power, turning one's will and power in upon themselves.

*4th Chakra. Grief:* Hinders the love and lightness of the heart, leaving a heavy burden on one's persona.

*5th Chakra. Lies:* Misinformation hinders our relationship to the world.

*6th Chakra. Illusion:* Looking at things incorrectly, not seeing the big picture, and seeing only what one wants to see, can hinder our perception.

*7th Chakra. Attachment:* Holding on to the pointless and focusing all of one's attention in one area can obscure the big picture and hinder our relationship with the divine.

# Appendix C

How our bodies feel to us every day communicates what we need to change in our life.

**The Chakra system** is a grouping of energies from the sacrum up to the ethers above your head. This is a discussion of the seven major chakras. There are many, smaller chakras as well. Healthy chakras spin in a clockwise fashion with equal speed. The chakra energy is smaller on the front of the body and is larger on the back, much like how a shotgun spreads its load when fired. To fix the chakras directly on the body the energy is usually directed from the front to back. The first step to healing is to acknowledge and witness the wound.

Each organ of the body has a particular time of the day it cycles. If the energy is balanced with the other organs of the body there are no problems or dis-ease in the body. If the energy is imbalanced with more energy going to it than normal it becomes irritated. If there is not enough energy to the organ, the body slows circulation and nervous stimulation in that organ and its function slows down.

## Here is a list of organs and their associated times:

11pm-1am Gallbladder/Pineal

1am-3am Liver

3am-5am Lungs

5am-7am Large Intestine (colon, rectum, appendix)

7am-9am Stomach/Muscles

9am-11am Spleen/Pancreas/Bone

11am-1pm Heart

1pm-3pm Small Intestine/Duodenum

4pm-6pm Nerves

3pm-5pm Bladder

5pm-7pm Kidney

8pm-10pm Blood

7pm-9pm Circulation-Sex/Adrenals/Reproductive glands/Skin/ Pituitary

9pm-11pm Thyroid/Triple Warmer/Pericardium/Thymus/Common Bile duct

The goal is to have balanced energies going to all organs at all times of the day for perfect health. **There are many ways to balance organ energy** including what you eat, supplements, drugs, emotional work, colour therapy, crystals, homeopathy, flower essences, drumming, reflexology and many other healing modalities.

# Bibliography

- *Wisdom of the Mystic Masters* by Joseph Weed
- *The Chakra Handbook* by Shalila Sharamon and Bodo J. Baginski
- *The Chakras* by C.W. Leadbeater
- *Eastern Body Western Mind* by Anodea Judith
- Organon of Medicine by S. Hahnnemann
- *The Spirit of Homeopathy* by R. Sankaran
- *The Science of Homeopathy* by G. Vithoulkas
- *Homeopathy and Energy* by Paul Francis